THE KILLER BEES

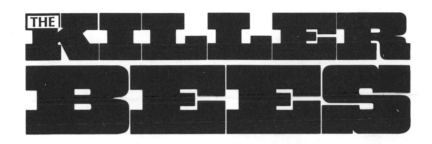

THE KILLER BEES

ANTHONY POTTER

GROSSET & DUNLAP
A Filmways Company
Publishers · New York

Copyright © 1977 by Anthony Potter
All rights reserved
Published simultaneously in Canada
Excerpts and photographs from the "Killer Bees" segment of NBC's
WEEKEND program, broadcast on June 7, 1975, are reprinted with
the permission of the National Broadcasting Company, Inc.
Library of Congress catalog card number: 76-15710
ISBN 0-448-12639-7 (hardcover)
ISBN 0-448-12640-0 (paperback)
First printing 1977
Printed in the United States of America

Dedication

This book is dedicated to my wife, Phyllis—a true believer from the start—and to my daughters, Whitney and Ashley, for their wonderful curiosity.

Acknowledgments

I would like to thank NBC News and Reuven Frank for allowing me to use NBC News research material. The story "Killer Bees" first appeared on American television on June 7, 1975, on the NBC News program "Weekend." I am extremely grateful to Reuven Frank, the executive producer of the show, who was the prime mover behind the television documentary and this book. I would also like to thank my editor at Grosset and Dunlap, Martin Torgoff, for his guidance and interest in the subject; researcher Rosemary Short for her contributions; and film editor Otto Pfeffer, who provided many of the still photographs taken from the television documentary.

Contents

The Department of Genetics at the University of São Paulo in Ribeirao Preto is experimenting with 4 million bees, trying to cross-breed a more gentle strain.

1

The Fantasy

Killer Bees Invade the United States

"Nature is a mutable cloud,
which is always and never the same."

Emerson

Miami

The banana boat *Cubahama* slipped slowly up the Miami River at 6 A.M. on a humid August morning. The city was just waking up. A U.S. Customs launch idled off the port stern of the ship, watching for any suspicious activity. The *Cubahama* had just come from the port of Cartegena, Colombia. The Customs Bureau had been tipped off that there would almost certainly be cocaine on board. Just four months ago Customs had seized 40 pounds of cocaine, worth about $10 million on the street. It had been one of the biggest busts in recent times. This time the contraband would not be cocaine.

The Killer Bees

New York

At 7 A.M. the same morning the sugar boat *Ciudad de Bucaramanga* had finished tying up at Pier No. 3 in Brooklyn. New York had been like a steambath all summer long. This August morning was no exception. It would be a blistering day. Worse, the city had been hit by a sanitation strike. It had been going on for ten days, and New York was permeated by the awful stench of old garbage piling up in the filthy streets.

Miami

At 7 A.M. sharp the U.S. Customs team boarded the *Cubahama*. One small group of men searched the bow, another the stern. The crew was assembled at midships, next to the main cargo hold. First, the inspectors would check the cargo. It was not unusual to find cocaine hidden in a bunch of bananas. The Customs team began a thorough search, knowing that the *Cubahama* had just come from Colombia, the cocaine-smuggling capital of the world.

One of the deckhands unhooked the hatch cover and slid it back. Inspector Dennis Bracken jumped down inside and disappeared in the forward part of the hold.

Suddenly there was a scream and a loud buzzing sound; actually it was more like a high-pitched roar—**zzziiiii**—Bracken was waving his arms frantically and running wildly, trampling boxes of bananas. He was covered by hundreds of angry, screaming bees.

As Bracken fell to the deck, the bees rose quickly, like a huge, vibrating blanket, and flew out of the hold to the dock, where they settled on some off-loaded crates of bananas.

Captain Paul Keough, who was in charge of the search party, ran to Bracken, now lying face down in the hold. Keough felt his pulse. Nothing. He turned Bracken over to try mouth-to-mouth resuscitation, but drew back in horror.

Bracken's face was swollen to twice its normal size and marked with huge red welts. His lips were bulbous, grotesque. As Keough opened Bracken's mouth, he saw bees crawling on his tongue and down his throat. They had flown into Bracken's mouth when he screamed for help.

Keough called the inspector from the Department of Agriculture. But he had no one available who knew how to handle a swarm of bees, so he advised Keough to contact Dr. Robert Henshaw, of the University of Florida's Entomology Department, one of the top bee experts in the country. Meanwhile, The Department of Agriculture would send someone from the Animal and Plant Health Inspection Service (APHIS) to the docks.

New York

The longshoremen at Pier No. 3 finished their coffee about 7:30 A.M. and boarded the sugar boat. Raw sugar was repugnant to dockhand Mike Austin, who detested its sickening, molasseslike smell. As he walked up the gangplank in the hot, humid weather, the sugar stuck to his shoes like tar.

He opened the main hold and gingerly climbed down to inspect the raw sugar. The ladder was sticky with melted sugar, which stuck to his hands. The sweet smell was overpowering. As Austin jumped to the deck at the bottom of the hold, about three feet lower than the end of the ladder, he suddenly became aware of a sharp buzzing sound—**zzziiiiii**. A swarm of bees had nested in the hold, lured by the raw sugar, and the prospect of an indefinite food supply.

Austin yelled, "Throw a line. Throw a line," and frantically grabbed for the lower rung of the ladder. His screams were muffled by the sound of bees. To the men on deck, he sounded as if he'd been gagged.

The dock foreman's first instinct was to close the hatch and trap the bees inside. He was allergic to bee stings and terrified of bees. But what about Austin, and what about the cargo? We've got to get Austin out of there, he thought.

The dockhands watched in horror as Austin flailed at the bees and screamed, "My God, my God! Help me, help me!" His face was contorted in agony, his eyes mere slits in his swelling face. The bees covered him, flying into his nose, ears, and mouth. His screams turned into uncontrolled sobbing; then he gasped for breath, and fell silent.

By the time the rescue crew reached Austin, got his body out, and sealed the hatch, the bees were gone. No one had seen them fly away, but they were gone.

Suddenly, it occurred to the Agriculture inspector, "My God, the garbage strike. New York is having a garbage strike."

Miami

Dr. Robert Henshaw was a noted entomologist. Scientists the world over sought his knowledge of bee behavior. But this case had him confused. What kind of bees were they? They looked like Italian bees, which are common in the United States, although they were slightly smaller. But Italian bees were not that aggressive. Could they be the African bees of South America?

Henshaw knew that a Brazilian geneticist had introduced aggressive African bees to Brazil, hoping to improve honey production by developing a hard-working but gentle hybrid. There had been an accident and several swarms of African bees had escaped and mated with local bees, producing extremely aggressive, vicious offspring. In just 20 years the killer bees had spread from São Paulo, Brazil, to Venezuela. There had been recent reports that the killer bees had reached Colombia. In the port city of Santa Marta a 12-year-old boy and a baby had been attacked and killed while picnicking with their parents. The mother and father had been hospitalized, but had survived.

Dr. Henshaw had been following the northward progress of the killer bees, plotting it on a large wall map. The killer bees apparently preferred the coastline to the inland areas. They had bypassed the desolate Guajira Desert of northeastern Colombia and moved to the port city of Santa Marta, then down the coast to Cartegena.

The *Cubahama* was from the port of Cartegena.

New York

An African queen bee can lay 5,000 eggs in one day. If the bees got a foothold in New York City, they would multiply beyond control. Inspector Kevin Murphy of the New York City Health Department knew this. Aware that with the garbage strike the bees would forage more frequently because of the abundant food supply, divide up into many swarms, and spread throughout the entire city within a few days, he moved swiftly to locate and exterminate them.

The bees had last been seen in the Sugar Terminal at Pier No. 3 in Brooklyn. If they could be quarantined there (and this was a remote hope), then perhaps a special "bee squad" could capture the queen and destroy the swarm. But there wasn't much time.

Inspector Murphy ordered the Sugar Terminal closed. His men sealed every crack and opening in the building with putty and gaffer's tape, and the special "bee squad" went inside. They were an eerie sight. In their protective clothing—hard hats, leather gloves, and heavy boots—the men looked like spacemen. They sprayed every square inch of the Sugar Terminal with Parathion, a deadly pesticide that has an effect like nerve gas.

In a last death gasp the bees attacked the men, stinging them through their protective clothing. Thousands of stingers were left in their leather gloves and coveralls, each from a bee that gave up its life in a fury to protect its queen and food supply. The pain was excruciating. Every time the bee fighters moved their arms to spray the pesticide, the coveralls would draw tight across their backs and shoulders. It was almost as though the bees knew this, and zeroed in on their victims' vulnerable spot.

The most frightening part of the attack was when the furious bees crashed by the thousands into the veils, sometimes only a fraction of an inch from the men's eyes. The bees clustered so thickly on the veils that the men could hardly see. Neither of them was squeamish and both were used to handling angry bees, but they had never experienced anything like this.

The pesticide started taking effect quickly, and the men took advantage of a lull in the attack to stagger outside the terminal. They were partly overcome by the pesticide, and partly by the bee stings.

Outside, medics administered oxygen and gave them adrenaline shots from emergency bee-sting kits. Bee venom acts on the respiratory system, causing anaphylactic shock. One bee sting can kill a person who is allergic to the venom (the throat closes and the victim suffocates). Fifty to one hundred bee stings can kill a person who is *not* allergic. The men on the special bee squad had been stung more than 100 times.

Inspector Murphy waited for the pesticide to take effect, then sent the bee squad back inside the Sugar Terminal. Thousands of dead bees lay strewn on the sticky floor of the warehouse. Almost overcome by the heat and the sickening smell of raw sugar and Parathion, the men undertook the painstaking job of trying to find the queen.

Miami

In Miami, Dr. Henshaw suspected that the bees from the *Cubahama* were killer bees. He was not positive because there was no foolproof method of identifying the bees quickly. Professor Howell Daly, of the University of California at Berkeley, had developed a system of identifying killer bees by computer, but it was a time-consuming process, involving dissecting dead bees and entering their precise measurements into the computer. Hardly practical, but Henshaw decided to send Dr. Daly a dead specimen anyway.

Miami in August is unbearably hot and humid, perfect weather for killer bees, which thrive in tropical climates. The hotter the weather, the more vicious the bees become.

It was imperative to keep track of the bees' progress. They would undoubtedly move north, then west, as they cleared Florida's panhandle. Dr. Henshaw set up a killer bee control center, with a large wall map of the southern United States. He contacted every known beekeeper in the state of Florida for help. He recruited the university's entire Biology Department to take phone calls from local police and to pinpoint locations on the map.

The bees must be contained in the state of Florida, Henshaw thought. His only hope of stopping them was to set up a line of defense 100 miles north of their forward movement. First, he would establish a perimeter of poison swarm boxes. When the bees nested in these deadly hives, they would consume poisoned honey and die. At the same time, an army of beekeepers would penetrate the perimeter and kill every African queen in sight. Next, there would be a sort of Maginot Line, which would be saturated with gentle Italian queens. Any killer bees that got through would mate with the Italians. The hope was that the offspring would be more gentle.

Genetics had created this problem, perhaps genetics could solve it.

New York

New York's Health Department team had finished the tedious job of examining every dead bee in the Sugar Terminal. They could not find the queen. This meant that she had already moved on with her swarm. If the queen or any of the African drones mated with Italian bees, the offspring would be aggressive. Murphy knew it was now too late to control the situation. He alerted all beekeepers in the New York area to be on guard. All he could do now was wait.

The next morning New Yorkers woke up and lazily began their Sunday routine. Few of them knew about the incident at Pier No. 3 in Brooklyn. The story had not made the Sunday editions of *The New York Times* or the *News*. Murphy hadn't wanted the story to get out yet. There would be enough panic and hysteria when it did get out, and he was hoping that by the time the presence of the killer bees became publicly known, he would have things under control.

Miami

Florida is dense with vegetation and bees. It is one of the leading states in honey production and the use of bees for crop pollination. It was a perfect target for the killer bees because they move fastest when they can mate with an existing bee population. Dr. Henshaw's plan was brilliantly conceived, but it didn't work. Killer bees' genes for aggression are so dominant that the offspring are always at least as vicious as the Africans. Because of this, the killer bees swept through the state of Florida, then moved north into Georgia and west to Louisiana. The bees swarmed excessively and were impossible to control in the "wild." They ignored the poison swarm boxes, preferring trees and empty buildings. Beekeepers destroyed thousands of them, but this hardly diminished the thousands of swarms that now spread through the United States.

Henshaw's wall map was covered with pins and he could see clearly that the situation was hopeless. A death had been reported for almost every swarm location. Hundreds of people had been killed in bee attacks.

New York

The worst horror was in New York City. Because it was unusually hot and humid, families jammed Central Park. The stench of old garbage attracted the bees to the central part of the city, where the restaurants are concentrated. Every street from Washington Square to Central Park, from Broadway to First Avenue, was lined with piles of rancid garbage, some ten feet high. The sanitation strike had been going on for two weeks. The New York Health Department was desperately trying to keep rats from infesting the city. No one had imagined that the worst problem would be killer bees.

The bees began to cover each festering heap of garbage. They nested in the awnings of posh restaurants like Romeo Salta, Orsini's, and La Grenouille, and in the doorways of apartment buildings, now unattended by the starched and proper doormen who normally kept watch. There was an outbreak of crime—lootings of abandoned stores, robberies, muggings—and bands of young toughs paraded through the streets, unchallenged by the police, who couldn't keep up with the chain of events. Industrious worker bees flew from the fetid stacks of garbage to their makeshift hives to deliver a full load of food. Soon, the nests became overcrowded, and swarms of killer bees left to set up home elsewhere.

In Central Park there was chaos. Several hundred swarms had nested in the park near the lake to be close to the water. People crowded into the park to cool off, not noticing the menacing bees in the surrounding trees. All it took was one incident and the bees, almost by universal signal, went berserk. A small child wading in the sailing pond threw a stick at one of the bee colonies in a tree. The bees attacked the child, a four-year-old boy, covering him with stings and killing him instantly. His distraught parents tried to rescue the child and fight off the attacking bees. This made the bees more angry, and they began attacking everyone in sight. People all over the park began screaming hysterically and running in all directions, their frenzy only further enraging the bees. Soon all of Central Park was one massive killer bee rampage. The bodies of the dead and the unconscious—mostly those allergic to bee stings—were strewn surrealistically beside the lake and along the paths and the walkways like human litter.

One man jumped into the lake and swam underwater to escape from the bees. He held his breath as long as possible, and when he came up for air on the other side of the lake, the bees covered his head and stung him to death. They had been tracking him as he swam underwater and hovered above the exact spot where he had to come up for air.

Miami

More and more reports of deaths came flooding into Dr. Henshaw's control center in Miami. What he had feared most was now happening. As the killer bees moved north and west, there was widespread panic. Vigilante groups sprang up, killing all the bees they could, mostly gentle, useful bees that were valuable for crop pollination. The vigilantes also attacked beekeepers, whom they blamed for the killer bee menace.

The most far-reaching effect of the killer bee invasion was economic. The invasion of the killer bees began to eliminate the use of bees for crop pollination, which would severely limit food production. United States agriculture would be dealt a crippling blow. Food prices would soon skyrocket, there would be food riots, and the economy would be devastated.

The killer bees had conquered the South and were moving rapidly westward. The bees in New York City were thriving and reproducing prolifically in the hot, humid August weather. *The New Yorker* magazine, in its "Talk of the Town" column, had flippantly referred to them as "the bees of August," but it was not a time for humor, even dark humor.

Scientists believed that killer bees could not survive in cold weather. When this fact became known, millions of people left their homes to go further north. Caravans of evacuees crowded the nation's highways, making the northeastern United States one huge traffic jam.

There were thousands of deaths that August and well into September, many of them caused by the panic that began to grip the East Coast. It had been a tragic affair, but the worst seemed over when the weather cooled off as the bees calmed down and prepared for winter. Residents of New England, the upper Midwest, and the Pacific Northwest felt safe from the killer bees. They were unaware of what had happened in Baton Rouge, Louisiana, on a warm, muggy day in September.

Baton Rouge

It was late afternoon, just after the Italian worker bees had returned from their busy day of collecting nectar. The African swarm moved quietly like a thick mat on the Bermuda grass around hive No. 343 at the National Bee Stock Center in Baton Rouge. Quickly, like a crack commando team, they flew from the grass into the hive. The African workers found the docile Italian queen and surrounded her in a relentless frenzy until she was engulfed in a ball, suffocated, and killed. The African queen then moved to the center of the hive. Italian workers moved nervously around her, did various forms of a "waggle dance," and settled down. They had accepted their vicious new queen. The gentle Italian drones mated with her during her first nuptial flight, and their offspring were nasty African hybrids. In turn, the drones produced by the hybrids mated with Italian queens, producing even more aggressive Africanized bees.

In one well-executed commando attack, the killer bees took over the National Bee Stock Center in Baton Rouge, Louisiana. The center provides young queen bees for restocking hives in the Spring throughout the northern United States and Canada.

Now the killer bees could invade the northern United States without anyone knowing it—until it was too late.

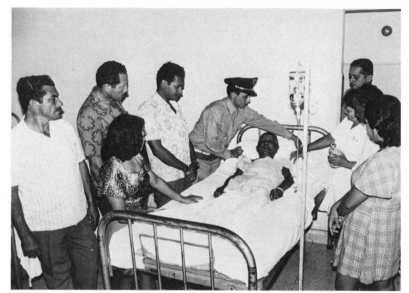

In 1974, Jose Ferreira was attacked by killer bees in Recife. Despite intensive medical treatment, he died in the hospital.

2

The Facts

Unfolding Tragedies

"Do not be angry with me if I tell you the truth."

Socrates: Plato's Apology

"The African bee is like a vicious dog. If you leave them alone, nothing will happen."

Resident of Austim,
São Paulo.

What you have just read is fiction. Based on extensive documentation of killer bee attacks and behavior, the preceding scenario, though seemingly a farfetched exercise in fantasy, is entirely possible.

What follows sounds like a science fiction story. It is not. It is true.

In 1965 a Brazilian geneticist, Dr. Warwick Kerr, introduced the African honeybee (*Apis mellifera adansonii*) to Brazil. His purpose was to breed a superior honeybee, a sort of "master race" that would work harder and produce more honey than the gentle European bee common to South America and the United States.

Unfortunately, African honeybees have two undesirable traits: they swarm excessively and they are extremely aggressive. Dr. Kerr's genetic experiment became a disaster of overwhelming proportions. It was (and still is) the greatest genetic experiment in history, and it backfired.

The viciousness of the African bee so disturbed Dr. Kerr that he quarantined the original African queens he brought to Brazil. At that time, the story goes, a mysterious accident occurred when a visiting beekeeper permitted 26 swarms of Kerr's bees, all led by African queens, to escape. He removed a small gate from the mouth of each hive, which is called a "queen excluder"; it prevents the larger queens and drones from getting out of the hive. The free African swarms disappeared in the wilds of São Paulo.

Since that time (1957) the African bees have mated with and absorbed all the bees in Brazil. The genes for aggressiveness in the African bee were so strong that they became dominant in the offspring, which turned out to be vicious and nasty.

The bees have killed as many as 300 people, attacked thousands of others, and stung to death thousands of farm animals and pets. They have taken over most of South America and are moving north at a rate of 200 miles a year. It was in Brazil that the insects earned the name "killer bees."

It is a real story, unfolding day by day in South America—the result of man tampering with nature.

As a television journalist, I was skeptical when I first became aware of the story through a short clipping in the *Wall Street Journal* headed "Killer Bees on Way North."

I started researching the story, reading newspaper and magazine accounts, and talking to scientists throughout the United States. By coincidence, I met with a team of scientists who had recently returned from Brazil, where they had studied the problem firsthand. The United States Department of Agriculture commissioned the scientists to prepare a report on the threat of the Africanized bee to the United States.

Their detached report was sobering. Killer bees were to be taken very seriously.

I traveled to Brazil to see for myself and produce a television documentary for NBC News, not realizing at the time that we would be the first to film an actual killer bee attack.

Brazil, and particularly Rio de Janeiro, is an unlikely place for a horror story. It is the land of the string bikini, the bossa nova, and "the beautiful people." As I gazed from my hotel room on the splendid bronzed *cariocas* (natives of Rio) in their *tangas* on Copacabana Beach, the threat of killer bees seemed far away.

But it is not far away; the bees are moving closer day by day. The subject has become highly controversial, thus it is best to start with facts—case histories of actual killer bee attacks.

It is important that you understand that what follows is not sensationalism, nor exaggerated reporting. It is accurate and it is documented.

Curitiba is in the southern part of Brazil in the state of Parana. It is rich farm country with a mild, temperate climate, except during the summer when it is hot, humid, and rainy. It was on such a rainy, hot day—December 3, 1973—that the killer bee attack occurred. The next day the incident made headlines in Curitiba's daily newspaper, *Gazeta do Povo.* The details were sketchy and did not tell the entire story:

African Bees Kill Farmer

Domingos Massucheto, 65 years of age, died Monday after being attacked by a swarm of African bees. The incident occurred in Ferraria, a small town near Campo Largo. Following an autopsy, the body was interred at Campo Largo Cemetery. This is not the first victim of these bees, according to government health officials. They are now returning with the arrival of summer.

Massucheto was a man of the soil who had worked as a farmer his entire life. He had one son in his twenties and a teenage daughter. Lately, he had been distressed that he could not exert himself because of a severe heart condition—arteriosclerosis—and depended on his son to help run the farm.

The Killer Bees

It was late afternoon when he was walking back from the fields after harvesting the summer corn. A swarm of killer bees had nested in the tile roof of his house. His dog was playing in the yard near the house and horses grazed in a nearby field. It was quiet and peaceful.

Suddenly, there was a loud, high-pitched buzzing sound—**zzziiiii**—and two horses reared up and whinnied in pain. The horses started running toward a cliff and the killer bees chased them. At first, the bees came in small groups, pursuing the horses like waves of dive bombers; then they massed in a huge swarm and covered the horses, looking like a clinging, writhing blanket. The bees killed the two horses, then turned on Massucheto's dog, covering it with stings. As the dog howled in pain, the farmer frantically ran to help it. The bees then attacked Massucheto, stinging him hundreds of times. He screamed in pain, then sobbed. His twitching body was covered with a throbbing layer of black insects, their angry buzzing muffling his screams. Bees crawled inside Massucheto's mouth and ears. His eyes were hidden behind swollen folds of puffy skin, irritated by the massive injections of bee venom. The farmer flailed at the bees, which only made them more angry.

Massucheto's weak heart could not stand the shock, the hysteria, the poison venom. He died within minutes, in a kneeling position, as if he were praying.

Mrs. Massucheto watched helplessly as the bees killed her husband. Her daughter, Ana, ran hysterically toward her father, then back toward the house; the mother grabbed the girl and took her inside. Mrs. Massucheto regained enough composure to call the local fire department. Her son, Antonio, was working in a distant field when he heard his father's screams. He raced to the scene—only to see his father's hideously swollen face, testimony of his last moments of agony and sheer terror.

Mrs. Massucheto later described the bees as "like a wild bull" when they attacked.

An autopsy was performed at the Institute of Legal Medicine in Curitiba. The attack was so vicious that 80 bees were found inside Massucheto's stomach. They had entered his mouth when he screamed.

The tenacious bees continued their furious attack for several hours, until the fire department drove them off using heavy smoke and strong insecticides.

Julio Pizzato had always lived a simple, devoutly religious life and, like many of the residents of the small port town of Antonina, he enjoyed basking in the warm sun on a park bench in Cavalcanti Square. The park was nestled beneath the town's church, which had a beautiful steeple. A cemetery was on one side of the park, and small tidy houses lined another side. The fourth side of the square was filled with idle taxicabs, their drivers standing around, relaxing, chatting, passing time.

Antonina is in the state of Paraná, located on the inner shore of the Bay of Paranagua. The town is surrounded by mountains and has a semitropical climate. It is almost always hot, with a sweaty humidity of 80 percent or higher. Antonina rarely gets fresh breezes, and on the sunny, spring day of October 17, 1971, the air was still.

Sixty-two-year-old Pizzato was a cripple, his left side totally paralyzed by a stroke one month earlier. He enjoyed sunning himself in the park; it made him forget his illness. He always considered the beautiful old church and cemetery with its elegant and ornate mausoleums his own private sanctuary. On that day a small boy was climbing the steeple, swinging a stick, unaware of a swarm of bees that had nested inside.

As Pizzato rested on the park bench, there was suddenly a loud buzzing sound . . . it became louder and louder. With difficulty, he managed to turn and look. What he saw was a swarm of killer bees, descending, like a huge dark mat, from the church's steeple. casting a dark shadow over the square.

In an instant, the angry swarm covered most of Cavalcanti Square. Everyone in the vicinity screamed and, in panic, ran for shelter. Some went inside their houses, the bees pursuing them; the taxi drivers jumped into their cabs and rolled the windows shut. The noise and hysteria made the enraged bees even more angry and they began stinging everyone and everything in sight. Even cats and dogs scampered frantically for hiding places.

The Killer Bees

As the taxi drivers watched from their cars, they saw a blurred tableau of people running, screaming, and waving their arms. One of them was 28-year-old Mrs. Ajadir Gomes, who was six months pregnant. As she was running, she fell on the street, stung several times.

They watched helplessly as the bees concentrated on Julio Pizzato, the cripple, who could not move from the park bench. The bees covered his entire body, stinging him more than 100 times.

A young man, Leoncio Estorachi, tried to help Pizzato and was himself stung 40 times in the head. He was driven off by the bees. Pizzato's brother and sister-in-law also ran to help, but in vain. Minutes after the killer bees attacked him, Pizzato fell from the bench. As he screamed for help in his terror, some bees flew into his mouth and were swallowed.

The cab drivers and other motorists poured oil and kerosene into their carburetors, hoping the thick black smoke would calm the vicious bees. Some attacked the bees with fire extinguishers, but their efforts were futile. Although the smoke held back the insects in flight, it had no effect on the bees covering Pizzato's body.

While the taxicabs spewed dense smoke, two drivers managed to drag the victim to one of the cars and drive him to the municipal first aid station.

The doctor on duty gave Pizzato first aid, and transferred him to Santa Cruz Hospital in Curitiba, 50 miles away. When the victim was put in a taxi (Antonia is too poor to afford an ambulance), a phenomenon occurred: for a few minutes, Pizzato was able to use his paralyzed left leg and move both legs simultaneously. This was undoubtedly an effect of the bee venom, but doctors would not speculate as to how it happened.

According to the official medical report:

Pizzato showed reactivation of the paralyzed portion of his body and then went into a coma. Despite intensive treatment and specialized medical care at Santa Cruz Hospital, he did not endure and died approximately 30 hours later.

He was buried in Antonina—in the cemetery next to Cavalcanti Square.

The killer bee attack in Antonina lasted two hours—from 10 A.M. to 12 noon. At the end of it, thousands of dead bees were strewn all over Calvalcanti Square and 30 people were injured, 3 of them seriously. Most of those stung repeatedly suffered from vomiting, itching, and varying degrees of visual disorder and shock.

On February 28, 1975, 12 passengers boarded a Voctec-Taxi Aero helicopter at the airport in Natal, a city on the northeast coast of Brazil near the equator. The passengers were going to visit an offshore oil-drilling platform owned by the Brazilian national petroleum consortium, Petrobas.

About 50 miles north of Natal, as the helicopter neared the coastline, the engine suddenly stalled. The helicopter crashed in a dense tropical thicket and the passengers, some already critically injured, were trapped inside the bent wreckage. The pilot, 29-year-old Milton Freitas, was knocked unconscious in the crash; the co-pilot dragged him out of the smoking helicopter and went back to rescue the passengers. He could hear their painful cries and groans, their fists banging on hot crushed metal, and their screams for help. As the co-pilot approached the helicopter, it burst into flames and exploded. The twelve passengers trapped inside were killed instantly.

The co-pilot retreated in horror, then grabbed the pilot and started to drag him through the thick jungle, both of them stunned and dazed. Suddenly, they heard a high-pitched **zzziiiii**, which grew louder and louder: it was a swarm of killer bees, which had been agitated by the helicopter crash.

The bees attacked the two men, who were already in shock. They managed to limp through the underbrush, trying to fight off the stinging bees. All they could hear was the relentless buzz of the bees, which tried to crawl inside their torn clothing, stinging their faces and necks. The two men undoubtedly would have been killed if the bees had not been attracted to the burning helicopter.

Finally, they reached a clearing; it was a farm and a tractor was plowing the field about 1,000 yards away. They stumbled toward the tractor, waving their arms, screaming for help.

The tractor driver was stunned at the sight of the two men, dazed and bleeding, their pilot's uniforms shredded, swatting at the bees that were still chasing them.

The Killer Bees

He took them to a hospital in the nearby town of Baizios, where they were given antihistamine tablets and shots of adrenaline for their bee stings, and medication for their cuts and bruises. Miraculously, they had survived both the crash and the killer bee attack.

They were kept under observation for several days, thankful to be alive, but shaken and permanently scarred by the grim experience.

Jacarepagua Lagoon is a dense tropical swamp noted for its unusual vegetation.

Professor Luis Emidio de Melo, Jr., a botanist with the National Museum, frequently went there to collect specimens. The afternoon of April 7, 1975; like previous field trips, was uneventful until Professor de Melo started to leave.

He was trudging through the thick underbrush, his samples in a knapsack, when a colony of killer bees attacked him. It happened in an instant; there was no more than one second between the warning—a loud buzzing—and the first sting.

Distraught, he tried to run, but got caught in a thicket of vines. He fell to the ground, trying to cover himself with dirt and dry leaves, crawling laboriously toward the edge of the lagoon. The bees continued attacking relentlessly as de Melo tried to scurry on all fours, swat at the bees, and cover his face—all at the same time. His mouth was dry and he could taste the dirt as he crawled toward the muck of the swamp.

By the time he reached the lagoon, all the exposed areas of his body, already swollen, had become large, painful sores, which seemed to attract an even greater number of the furious bees. He felt as if his entire body was on fire. The loud, intense **zzziiiii** echoed in his ears; his puffy eyes were moist and glazed and he had trouble focusing.

Finally, after an incredibly strenuous effort while suffering from intense pain, de Melo escaped from the bees by diving into the mud at the edge of the lagoon. He covered his head with his shirt, but the bees kept stinging him through the material. He tried covering the shirt with mud, but the bees continued stinging his arms. Finally, he plastered himself with the mud, covering his entire body and face. He realized he had to make a hole in the mud for breathing, and as he did, the persistant bees quickly found it and tried to fly inside his mouth. Lying face down in the mud with his arms over his head, he prayed that the bees would let up, afraid that death was near. Professor de Melo stayed awake in horror all night, cringing in a fetal position in the mud, occasionally drinking water squeezed from the stalks of swamp lilies and eating giant fern buds to survive. By morning, the bees were gone, and he had enough strength to reach his car, which was parked nearby.

When he arrived home his family was both relieved and shocked. When he had not come home, they thought he had been kidnapped and contacted the police. They didn't recognize this mud-covered apparition with the hideously swollen face as he stood before them in mute horror.

Suzano is a small suburb of the industrial city of São Paulo. Its main street, Rua Francisco Glicero, is lined with busy shops. April 7, 1975, began as a routine day. Antonio da Silva watered down and swept the pavement in front of his shoe store, then relaxed with a cup of coffee; it was 10 A.M., and in Brazil that means time for coffee.

Across the street, workmen were repairing the roof and replacing the gutters of the old building at 679 Rua Francisco Glicero. As one of the workers, Antonio Libonati, pulled a rotted gutter away from the building, several columns of bees flew out and began stinging him and another worker. Both scurried down their ladders quickly and ran away from the building. They were not badly stung and did not realize that they had unleased an incredible chain of events.

The angry bees turned on the first person they could find, a poor ragpicker who happened to be passing by the building. The killer bees covered him with stings and he fell, unconscious. More enraged bees flew out from the rooftop behind the gutter where they had been nesting. A police car also in the vicinity rescued the ragpicker and took him to a hospital. By this time, the furious bees had grown in number and become a hovering, menacing swarm—like an enormous black manta ray floating down the street—darting up and down, drifting back and forth, stinging shoppers at random before they realized what was happening.

Then the panic set in. As shopkeepers locked their doors and people ran from the Rua Francisco Glicero, the swarm became bolder and more angry, attacking scores of shoppers and bewildered, confused onlookers.

Shoe store owner Antonio da Silva said everybody ran in different directions. "I never saw anything like it, I remembered scenes of a film in which a city was destroyed by an earthquake. I hid in the bathroom."

Someone had notified the police and fire departments, but they were helpless against the rampaging bees. Three trucks carrying ten soldiers arrived on the scene, but since they had no equipment nor any means of fighting the bees, all they could do was help to evacuate the victims and close off the side streets in an attempt to contain the bees. Policemen and firemen from Suzano were able to rescue many of the victims. The ten most serious cases were taken to hospitals in Suzano and the neighboring town of Mogi das Cruzes. Two of the military policemen were stung so badly that they, too, were hospitalized.

It was a scene of mass confusion, almost comic . . . with policemen, firemen, and soldiers running wildly about . . . victims screaming and fleeing in panic . . . shopkeepers peering from behind closed windows . . . and no one really knowing what to do, everyone at the mercy of the bees. Compounding the confusion, the Suzano chief of police instinctively called the São Paulo Fire Department, assuming that the large city had a bee squad, which most towns and cities in Brazil have because of the threat of killer bees. It turned out that São Paulo did not have a bee squad, nor the proper insecticides or flamethrowers for fighting bees. The desk sergeant in São Paulo gave the police chief in Suzano the name of a private company that could supply the necessary equipment. Enraged and frustrated, the police chief slammed down the telephone . . . then composed himself enough to call the fire department of the closest town, Magi das Cruzes.

Fortunately, Mogi das Cruzes had a bee squad and sent a team of five men, wearing special protective clothing—heavy coveralls, boots, leather gloves, wire mesh bee veils, and helmets—and equipped with flamethrowers and aerosol spray guns filled with a powerful insecticide. When the squad arrived the men were appalled at the scene—victims staggering in the street, rubbing their eyes, choking, coughing, overcome, not by bee stings, but by tear gas. Earlier, it seems, the State Police, in panic and confusion, had thrown tear gas bombs at the bees. The gas had no effect on the bees whatsoever.

The bee squad rescued the remaining victims and moved in to attack the killer bees. By 5 P.M. they had made some progress, but there were still thousands of bees in the shopping area. The bees were so tenacious and persistent that it took the firemen the entire night to either kill them or drive them off. The street looked like a battle scene—army jeeps and trucks blocked off side streets, clouds of tear gas hung in the air, debris cluttered the sidewalks.

When the battle was over, the bees were clearly the victors: 26 people were sent to hospitals, scores of others were injured, and hundreds were terrified. Among those hospitalized were the commander of the State Police, two radio car patrolmen, and one fireman.

The two laborers who had triggered the bee attack were unharmed and read about the incident in the newspaper the next morning.

At 5 P.M. on the warm, muggy afternoon of December 5, 1973, a funeral procession solemnly wound its way through the ornate tombstones and crypts in Rio de Janeiro's Caju Cemetery. The cemetery's energetic but frail young funeral director, Francisco Costa, led the silent cortege. Although he was only 33 years old, Costa was suffering from tuberculosis in both lungs, and had been released from a sanitorium only one month earlier. He was worried about his health, and feared he might soon join the hundreds of deceased he had escorted to their graves.

Caju Cemetery was crowded that afternoon: several hundred mourners were praying or singing burial chants at nearby gravesites. Costa was headed for Plot No. 75046; a memorial service was being held next to it at Plot No. 75045. As Costa's funeral procession approached the gravesite of the deceased, a swarm of aggressive bees suddenly loomed in front of the cortege. The swarm darted in and out of mausoleums, disappearing for a few seconds, then bursting from behind a large, imposing cross and hanging in the air in front of the funeral procession. Funeral Director Costa, terrified that his weakened body could not survive a bee attack, instinctively threw a handful of dirt at the bees.

This enraged them, and instantly they launched a vicious attack on the mourners, sending them screaming and running in all directions. The bees attacked everyone in the vicinity, nearly 300 people in all, creating a scene of wild, tumultuous confusion.

What happened next was truly incredible. Half the mourners screamed and tried to run away. The other half, although in pain from multiple bee stings, were more angered at the funeral director who threw the dirt that incited the bees. They chased Costa, grabbed him, and started beating him. At that point Costa was a rather confused man. He was in pain both from the bee stings and the beating from the angry mourners: he feared both the killer bees and the "killer mob."

The funeral director escaped by running to the cemetery administration building and locking himself inside. Two hours later police rescued him from the angry mob and escorted him safely home.

Later the fire department bee squad arrived, and in the eerie darkness killed the bees with flaming butane torches.

The mourners were undaunted: they demanded another chance to bury their beloved—this time with dignity.

José de Lima, of Austim, a São Paulo suburb, had been worried lately about his finances. He was 38 years old, held a job as a chauffeur for a publishing company, and had a wife and six children to feed. On the morning of September 2, 1972, de Lima and his wife, Dora, were on an early morning walk when they saw an unusual object lying in a vacant field, next to a tree. As they walked closer, they could see that it was a beehive, which must have fallen from the tree. There were bees inside (they could hear the muffled buzzing and feel the beehive vibrate), but no sentries bothered to survey the de

Limas, so they assumed it was safe to pick up the beehive. De Lima gingerly carried it home and put it in a wooden box nailed to a tree in the backyard. He was pleased with his find, thinking he could earn some extra money for his family by selling the honey.

Then the trouble began: they were killer bees.

The vicious bees started attacking neighbor's pets and farm animals—killing chickens, ducks, dogs, and cats. The neighbors pleaded with de Lima to get rid of the bees. They warned him of the danger of keeping them, but he paid no attention, saying that in a few days there would be excellent honey for everyone.

A few days later de Lima's six young children—aged four to eight—were playing in the backyard while the parents were away. Curious about the bees, one of the children poked the beehive with a bamboo stick. The next few moments were sheer terror for the distraught children.

A next-door neighbor, Mrs. Anita Pereira Damasceno, was cooking in her kitchen when she heard the shrill screams. She ran to the de Limas' backyard, grabbed as many children as she could and pushed them into the house. The children were crying for their parents, hysterical, trying to protect their faces from the painful stings. But they were helpless against the efficient and overwhelming enemy, their tender flesh no match for the barbed stingers and toxic venom. As they slapped at the bees, they inadvertently injected more poison into their bodies by squeezing the venom sacks at the end of the stingers. De Lima's seven-year-old son Sydney was covered with bees, his face grotesquely swollen.

Sydney died at the hospital; he had been stung more than 60 times. His brothers and sisters were in serious condition and remained hospitalized for several days.

More than 20 others—all of them neighbors—were stung by the rampaging bees. Two women were stung so badly that their faces were swollen and marked with large, ugly, red welts. They said they had become accustomed to African bees, which were now commplace in the town of Austim.

When de Lima arrived home and learned of the death of his son, he held his head in anguish and grief, blaming himself for the tragedy. He was sobbing uncontrollably as he lit the rolled-up newspaper and burned the beehive in his backyard.

In order to film an extremely nasty colony of killer bees in Recife, the NBC News crew had to buy special protective clothing. American bee suits and gloves proved inadequate, and camerman Aaron Fears had to line his veil with gaffer's tape for protection against the vicious bees. This was the only way he could take pictures.

3

The Center of the Storm

Attacked in Recife

"It is impossible to describe the feeling . . . you stand frozen, afraid to move, they keep coming after you in wave after wave, an unrelenting attack that never stops . . ."

The author,
after trying to film killer bees.

These are not isolated incidents. Some experts in Brazil estimate that as many as 300 people have been killed by the bees, and that thousands of others have been attacked and survived. No official records of bee attacks have been kept, so it is difficult to determine the exact number of deaths. Many attacks in the rural back country of Brazil are never reported, so the figures could be higher.

In the first few years after the 26 swarms escaped in 1957, there were isolated incidents in the state of São Paulo. Dr. Warwick Kerr, who introduced the bees into Brazil, did not inform the public of the situation. He was afraid of widespread panic; also, he did not know how aggressive and dangerous the killer bees would become.

The year 1962 was the real turning point: several attacks were reported in the state of Rio de Janeiro and it became clear that the killer bees were spreading. The public became alarmed. Because the bees native to Brazil are the stingless variety, Brazilians were used to gentle bees and could not comprehend the vicious and often unprovoked attacks.

In one of the early attacks in 1962 a swarm of bees nested in the tile roof of a Spanish stucco house on Governor's Island, near Rio's international airport. A maid was cleaning the house when the bees attacked and killed the owner's dog. The maid fainted. A neighbor called the fire department, which was not then equipped to fight the killer bees. The firemen brought butane torches, but decided against using them because they were afraid of setting the house on fire. They did not carry pesticides then, so they tried spraying the bees with cold carbon dioxide gas in fire extinguishers. This made the bees more angry, and they turned on the firemen. Two firemen were stung so badly that they had to be hospitalized.

Earlier, this same colony of bees had killed 15 hens on Governor's Island and chased workmen from a building under construction. When the fire department arrived, the men sprayed the bees with flaming gasoline. The bees retreated, but later returned. This time, a team from the Ministry of Agriculture was called to the scene, armed with a lethal insecticide. The poison spray finally overwhelmed the bees.

There were several other killer bee attacks in the state of Rio de Janeiro at about the same time.

In the small town of Itaboraí, near Rio de Janeiro, a swarm of bees attacked farmworker Leonardo de Matos while he was working in a field. The noise of his tractor incited the bees, which came out of nowhere and viciously struck, covering de Matos' entire body. He ran frantically. In desperation, he even set fire to his shirt with a match and a can of kerosene.

The mayor of Itaboraí happened to be visiting the farm that day. He watched in horror as de Matos ran, screaming, his shirt on fire, covered with bees. The mayor grabbed a fire extinguisher and cautiously moved toward the farmworker, aiming the extinguisher at the mass of bees. The bees then attacked the mayor, who had to run for his life. The farmworker fell to the ground.

A postmortem revealed that de Matos had been stung 1,000 times. The bees killed two cows, a horse, and several pigs, then they attacked a bus heading for Rio de Janeiro. They stung several passengers before the bus driver could build up enough speed to outrun the bees.

That same year, 1962, there were many attacks throughout Brazil, causing grave concern that the killer bees were spreading beyond control.

A farmer and a hiker were killed near the town of Vassouras, near Rio de Janeiro. The farmer's wife and son, who were traveling with them, escaped by running into a dense thicket of woods. When the wife returned to the road about half an hour later, she found the swollen body of her husband lying face down. The hiker had fallen dead in a roadside ditch.

Earlier in the year another farmer was killed by bees near São Paulo. Sixty people, most of them neighbors, tried to fight the bees and were seriously stung. They had not realized that their efforts were only aggravating the bees. The entire neighborhood lived in fear of the killer bees for several months.

Those same bees, almost as though they were holding a grudge, killed two dogs, five cats, and a dozen chickens before neighbors were able to drive them away with a smoke screen of burning leaves and old rags.

In one of the more spectacular early attacks, on September 16, 1965, a colony of killer bees invaded the main business section, Rio Branco, in downtown Rio de Janeiro. Rio Branco is the city's movie district, similar to Times Square in New York.

The swarm hung like a huge black canopy over the front of the Armed Forces Military Command building. People on the streets, including soldiers, panicked and ran in all directions, their shirts pulled over their heads to protect them from the marauding bees.

The killer bees drove sentries from their machine-gun posts, then began attacking civilians in the street. The bees stung more than 60 *cariocas* in the bold midafternoon attack. After they were finally dispersed with pesticides, dead insects lay strewn on the busy street for several days, a reminder that the vicious bees will attack anywhere, anytime.

That same year, in May, a resident of Caicira, near São Paulo, tried to burn an African beehive in the chimney of a local bar. The subsequent attack was reported in *Time* magazine, the first article on killer bees published in the United States.

Time described the attack as follows:

In a "buzzing mass that darkened the sun," one man reported, the Africans swarmed into the bar, stung a traveling wine salesman senseless, left so many stingers in the bald dome of the bartender that he "thought he was growing hair again." In three hours the bees stung 500 people. Then they buzzed off across nearby farms, where they left behind flocks of dead chickens, a dozen writhing dogs, and two horses so badly stung that they could not eat for three days.

1965 was a critical year for killer bee attacks; by that time, swarms had gathered strength and taken over local bee populations. In 1965 the vicious bees killed 50 people in the state of São Paulo. The public became increasingly alarmed, even panicked, at the prospect of the marauding insects spreading further. Dr. Warwick Kerr tried to solve the problem through genetics, hoping to cross-breed a more gentle bee. The government of Brazil did very little to help, however, and there was no concerted effort to fight the bees. We now know that Dr. Kerr's efforts failed.

By the end of 1965 the bees had reached Recife, on the northeast coast of Brazil near the equator, about 2,000 miles from Rio. They seemed to like the tropical humid climate, which is similar to that of their African homeland, and multiplied quickly. Within four years—by 1969—they had spread to Forteleza, farther north, and to Belém, at the mouth of the Amazon River.

The Amazon River was supposed to be a natural barrier. It wasn't—killer bees crossed the Amazon in 1971. They continued their move northward at a rate of 200 miles a year, and have already reached Venezuela. This has been confirmed by the Venezuelan Ministry of Agriculture.

In 1972, just 15 years after the 26 African queens escaped, killer bees had spread throughout Brazil, and every state, both in the north and south, had reported bee attacks. There seemed to be no pattern, although in 1972 there was a concentration of incidents in Recife and Fortaleza. Experts in Brazil noticed that the bees seemed more aggressive in northern Brazil near the equator. This was confirmed by a team of American scientists who went to Brazil to study the problem in late 1971. They did not know why.

In 1972 there was a bizarre killer bee attack at a small farm outside Recife. A swarm of bees became unexpectedly irritated and attacked several farm animals, killing two horses, three burros, five goats, and a dog. The bees then went after the farmer, his wife, and children, covering them with painful stings. They ran into the house to escape from the bees, and the distraught farmer grabbed his shotgun.

A neighbor who had heard the commotion ran over to help. The farmer was so confused that when he fired his shotgun at the bees, instead of hitting them, he shot his neighbor in the face. The neighbor survived, but lost an eye.

The farmer and his family also survived, but the farm looked like the aftermath of a germ warfare attack: dead animals lay strewn on the ground, their bodies swollen and pockmarked from the toxic bee stings.

They looked like victims of nerve gas. Death was caused by suffocation: as they went into severe anaphylactic shock, their nerves and muscles were no longer able to control their breathing. They twitched, then fell limp to the ground, their bodies twisted into grotesque shapes.

It was a grim sight, which left the farmer and his wife in tears. The land and the animals were their livelihood, all they owned. Now, the animals were gone.

One year later, also near Recife, a dense cloud of African bees unleashed a mass attack in the town of Goiana. The bees covered a 78-year-old man, José Dias, with stings and attacked 130 others in the town. Local police and firemen were unable to destroy the bees or curtail the vicious attack. The angry insects continued stinging people for several hours into the night in an area almost a mile wide.

The most seriously stung victim, José Dias, died 10 hours later in a local hospital. According to the medical report, he was stung more than 2,000 times.

The Killer Bees

Before leaving for Brazil to pursue the killer bee, I had heard that they were aggressive and that unprovoked attacks were common, but I had no idea how vicious they could be. Several bee experts in the United States warned me to take adequate protective clothing, so we bought the finest available from A. I. Root and Company, the leading manufacturer of beekeeping equipment. Our outfits consisted of white cotton coveralls with zippers (the bees even enter button holes), veils that zipped onto our coveralls, boots that covered our ankles, and light-colored soft leather gloves, which proved to be a mistake. As it turned out, our American protective clothing was far from adequate.

I spent three weeks in Brazil in search of the killer bee. My quest inevitably led me to Recife, where there had been several recent attacks. My own experience underscores the viciousness of these bees, although when I arrived in Recife, a sleepy, tropical port city with a large Negro population and a *Black Orpheus* feeling to it, I was heady with the excitement of the chase and my abstract fear of the bees lay in a state of suspended animation. The air was heavy and still when we arrived at our hotel near the beach. The houses and buildings gave the city a decayed, colonial look, occasionally punctuated by a stark modern supermarket or office building. Recife is a curious mixture of old and new. The days when sugar was king and slavery a common practice are a faded memory.

Killer bee attacks are so common in Recife that the fire department bee squad averages four house calls a day to destroy swarms that have nested in rooftops, in abandoned automobile bodies, in empty buildings, and in trees—killer bees are vagabonds and will live anywhere.

I had asked the head of Recife's Beekeeping Cooperative, Jaime Nascimiento, to help us find some extremely aggressive colonies of Africanized bees. Conventional beekeeping had been wiped out in Recife because native beekeepers could not manage the nasty African hybrids. Several beekeepers formed the cooperative to teach methods of handling killer bees, hoping to revive the honey industry.

I wanted to find a vicious colony of bees in order to film an aggressiveness test. This consists of dangling a black leather pouch in front of a hive and observing both how long it takes the bees to attack the pouch and how many stingers are left in it. I had bought a black suede jeweler's pouch and decided to place a wireless radio microphone inside it to record, for the first time, the sound of enraged killer bees attacking and stinging. We did not know it at the time, but we would also record the bees' "death cry" as they lost their stingers and died. A bee dies in the act of stinging because when the barbed stinger and venom sack are ripped from its body, the bee is literally disemboweled. It can still fly around for as long as one hour, then it falls to the ground. One of the most incredible phenomena of the insect world is that the bundle of muscles around the poison sack continues to pump even after being detached from the body of the bee. One beekeeper, A. I. Root of Medina, Ohio (author of *The ABC and XYZ of Bee Culture*), observed muscles contracting and pumping venom for more than 20 minutes after being pulled from the bee. The muscles pump with enough power to push the barbed stinger through a felt hat or into a tough buckskin glove.

Bees are attracted to dark objects, African bees more so than others. They regard a black pouch or ball as an enemy, and how quickly and viciously they attack it is an accepted method of measuring their aggressiveness.

The morning we were to film the aggressiveness test was fearful and uneasy; the anxiety affected everyone, cameraman Aaron Fears, soundman José Valle, assistant cameraman Rick Malkums, and unit manager Ken Koerner. We had a light lunch on the veranda of the Hotel Miramar, next to the swimming pool. We gathered our gear, making sure each person had his protective clothing and an emergency bee-sting kit; then we boarded our two Volkswagen Combis and headed for a primitive apiary almost 25 miles outside of Recife. It was a remote area, overgrown with heavy tropical vegetation. The apiary itself was poorly kept. About 30 hives of aggressive African hybrids were at the bottom of a small arroyo behind a farmer's house. There were several small poor houses in the area, a few horses and cows, the usual chickens and young children, who were curious about these strangers dressed in white suits, carrying unusual machines.

The bees had a reputation for being nasty and uncontrollable. All of us were nervous, except our guide, Antonio Both, an experienced Brazilian beekeeper, who was not afraid of Africanized bees.

The Killer Bees

We dressed carefully, stepping into our coveralls, making sure our veils were tightly zipped to the collars of the coveralls and taping closed every opening or possible opening in our clothing. Killer bees have an extraordinary ability to find and enter any orifice in order to sting an enemy.

We had to tape the tops of our boots, our gloves, and our veils, even the slits in our coverall pockets, which contained our emergency bee-sting kits. As we adjusted our clothing and checked out the camera equipment, I went over our emergency procedure with the camera crew. Each of us carried a bee-sting kit containing antihistamine tablets, a tourniquet, alcohol, cotton, and a syringe filled with adrenaline. If one of us was stung repeatedly or proved to be allergic to bee-stings, the nearest person would give the victim an adrenaline shot. The person farthest away would go for medical help, while the others would help evacuate the victim.

The beehives were only about 200 yards from the farmer's house; the area was overgrown with banana palms. We walked cautiously down the hill and carefully approached the hives in order to drop the leather pouch in front of one of them.

Before we reached the hives, the bees attacked us. We were at least 100 yards from the nearest hive and did not even have our camera in position to film the aggressiveness test when the bees surged forward in a torrent, boiling at us as though they had exploded from a pressure cooker. They met us head-on in an overwhelming attack that left us confused and terrified.

The air was full of angry, screaming bees, bouncing off our veils inches from our eyes, enveloping our gloves and coveralls, piercing our protective clothing with their barbed stingers; the high-pitched **zzziiiii** was deafening and I felt the tingly, queasy sensation of insects crawling on my veil next to my neck. They crashed into us in a kamikaze fury, looking for any openings, any way to penetrate our defenses, to drive us away.

Our cameraman, Aaron Fears, tried to film the attack, but as he put his eye to the viewfinder of the camera, it pressed his veil flat against his face, which the bees were able to sting at will every time he tried to get a shot. They also stung his shoulders as he moved his arms, because the coveralls were too tight. Most surprising of all was the fact that the bees were able to sting us through our leather gloves. The soft leather, which protects against the stings of the more gentle European bees common in the United States, was ineffective against Africanized bees. Apparently the muscles around the sack and stinger of killer bees are more powerful, and push the stinger forward with greater thrust.

The enraged bees stung Aaron Fears so badly on his forehead, cheeks, hands, and shoulders that he dropped his camera in excruciating pain. (Ironically, when he returned to the United States after the killer bee assignment, Aaron volunteered to go to Saigon during the fall of South Vietnam. Each day he fearlessly dodged bullets and mortar shells on Route No. 1 north of Saigon and filmed the evacuation of the capital as it fell to the Vietcong. He was one of the last to leave that harrowing scene, but swears to this day that filming killer bees in Brazil was worse.)

It is impossible to describe the feeling of being attacked by 10,000 frenzied bees. Their loud buzzing—**zzziiiii**—drowns out all other sound . . . they **zit, zit, zit** as they pelt you and bounce off . . . they crawl on the netting around your face, blurring your visibility, probing for any opening which you may have forgotten to tape. You shudder as you glance down and see hundreds of stingers imbedded in your coveralls and gloves, knowing that 50 bee stings could kill you. You stand frozen, afraid to move, and the killer bees keep coming at you in wave after wave, an unrelenting attack, at full fury. You have a feeling of claustrophobia, fear that the attack will never let up, that you will not be able to escape the bees. You have trouble breathing, but remain still, trying not to panic. You reassure yourself that the bee-sting kit is in your pocket with the life-saving adrenaline syringe—but would you use it . . . could you use it?

All the while these fears and doubts flash through your mind, it is unbearably hot in the protective clothing and every movement attracts more bees. I was perspiring profusely and could no longer see through my fogged glasses and the dense cloud of bees covering my veil and darting around my head. We retreated slowly, getting several shots of the attack before being driven away.

Our guide, Antonio Both, managed to get near one hive and dangle the black suede pouch in front of the hive's opening. The irate bees covered the pouch, which took more than 1,000 stings in less than one minute. Being an experienced beekeeper, Antonio had casually underestimated the ferocity and tenacity of Africanized bees. He had neglected to tape his pants over his ankles; the bees penetrated under his trousers and socks, stinging his ankles badly. Even the stoic and brave Antonio had to give up, his ankles swollen and covered with red welts.

Because the bees are attracted to dark objects, they covered the camera, lens, and tape recorder. When we later played the audio tape of the attack, it was Antonio who recognized the high-pitched "death cry" of dying bees losing their stingers. It was a barely audible, high-frequency whine—**eeeiiiii** mixed in with **zzziiiii**—and it took trained ears to discern the eerie sound.

While we were filming, a curious chicken nearby was watching the weird tableau. The bees covered the chicken with stings; it wandered aimlessly in a daze for a few minutes, enduring terrible punishment, then it died. We retreated toward the farmer's house, hoping that the bees would not attack the children. Fortunately, the doors were locked and the family safe inside. We ran to our VW buses, threw the camera equipment in, and drove off, still in our cumbersome bee outfits.

The next day we heard that the enraged bees had continued attacking people in a small village one mile away for several hours into the night. The villagers, we were told, went to church and prayed that we would never return.

Their prayers were answered.

Still smarting from the vicious attack, we did decide to try again the next day—but this time in a different location, at a different apiary, whose bees were still aggressive, but not quite as nasty.

In order to film these killer bees, we had to buy heavier protective clothing; rubber parkas with hoods to wear under our coveralls, and heavy leather gloves that reached our elbows, like gauntlets. We also had to line the cameraman's veil with heavy tape, leaving only a slit over one eye to see through. He looked and moved like a moon-walker, and I could not help recalling Louis Hayward in the movie *The Man in the Iron Mask.*

At least this time we were adequately protected.

The film from the first attack and the next day contained remarkable close-up shots of the bees attacking the camera lens, the leather pouch, and us. It was the first time that killer bees had ever been filmed.

Dr. Warwick Kerr, a noted geneticist, first introduced African bees into Brazil in 1956. His purpose was to improve honey production, because African bees produce more honey than the standard European honeybee. Dr. Kerr and his colleagues are now trying to genetically produce a more gentle strain and breed the aggressiveness out of the Brazilian hybrids.

4

The Perpetrator

Dr. Kerr and the African Queens

> "We are not the first
> Who, by our good intentions,
> do incur the worst."
>
> King Lear

Dr. Warwick Kerr is something of an enigma. At the time I interviewed him he was head of the Department of Genetics at the University of São Paulo, at the Ribeirão Prêto campus, about 100 miles northwest of the city of São Paulo. He is a widely known geneticist and is highly respected. He has few peers in the field of bee behavior.

Dr. Kerr is also a profoundly religious man, a Methodist living in the world's largest Catholic country. His critics have accused him of being strongly anti-Catholic, which he denies. He taught Sunday school faithfully before the regular Sunday service at the Methodist church in Ribeirão Prêto. He reportedly did not miss a Sunday in ten years. I attended his last Sunday school class. Dr. Kerr stood in front of a blackboard and summarized what he had taught his parish in the past decade. It seemed like a biology lesson.

What came across most strongly was a doctrinaire approach to religion that accommodates Kerr's profession as a geneticist, one who changes nature. He believes in God as the Creator of all things, and he also believes in evolution. And furthermore, that when God created man He endowed him with the liberty and freedom to create. He subscribes to what he calls "a biological concept of the species," as a population of beings that intermarry and produce fertile offspring, and that also has its own system of communication. Kerr believes in original sin, and that any type of sin damages man's relationship with God and requires reconciliation. He insists that religion and the science of genetics are compatible.

Dr. Kerr is of German and American descent. His ancestors fled the South after the Civil War in the United States and settled in Brazil. They lived with about 200 other families in a town they named Americus. Even today the colony celebrates the Fourth of July with a picnic, where they serve fried chicken, wave Confederate flags, and sing "Dixie."

I had only four days to fly to Brazil, locate Dr. Kerr, and interview him. He was about to leave for Manaus, near the heart of the Amazon, where he would be director of the National Institute for Amazon Research. The government of Brazil had offered him the post at a very high salary for five years and he admits that "it was an offer I couldn't refuse." Some critics think that because he is responsible for the introduction of the killer bees into Brazil, and in view of recent bad publicity on that score in the United States, the government chose to remove him from the scene tactfully. The Amazon is the perfect place for such an exile. In his new work Dr. Kerr is no longer involved in bee genetics.

The most striking thing about Dr. Kerr is his absolute confidence and unswerving faith in science. He is a man of good humor and considerable charm. He stands a little over six feet tall, is slightly stout and paunchy, and has the disheveled look of a scientist with too much on his mind to worry about dress. On the surface he doesn't appear to be bothered by the genetic catastrophe he unleashed, but privately he is in anguish.

It all began back in 1956, the year that Dr. Kerr won the Dreyfus Prize for his work in bee genetics. The prize gave him enough money to buy a microscope, a camera, and a plane ticket to Africa. At about the same time, the Brazilian Association of Beekeepers had asked the government to import some African honeybees, which they had heard were more productive than the bees in Brazil. The Brazilian Ministry of Agriculture asked Dr. Kerr to bring back some African queens and to begin experiments. At the time Dr. Kerr knew that African bees were aggressive, but not *how* aggressive.

Once in Africa, he soon realized that African bees were extremely fierce. He collected some samples from Tanzania and South Africa, 133 bees in all, selecting only the queens of successful African beekeepers, carefully screening them for gentleness. Then came the first unfortunate accident that befell Dr. Kerr. While en route to Brazil, a Portuguese Customs agent sprayed the bees with DDT in Lisbon and they arrived in Brazil dead. Perhaps this was an evil portent. Dr. Kerr, terribly upset and frustrated, reportedly chose the next batch at random, without screening out the more vicious bees.

Of the 70 African queens shipped from Africa, only 47 survived the trip to Brazil. Dr. Kerr warned the Brazilian government that the bees were more fierce than he had thought and should be quarantined. He transferred 35 pure African colonies (*adansonii*) to a eucalyptus forest in the state of São Paulo.

Originally, Kerr had planned to give the African queens directly to beekeepers, but when he realized how fierce they were, decided to improve them genetically, first. He planned to mate the African queens with gentle Italian drones, then breed the hybrids with Italian drones again in order to get rid of the genes for aggressiveness and keep the genes for productivity—in other words, he wanted to produce a hard-working, gentle bee. There was, and still is, no question in his mind that this could be achieved "with absolute predictability." In theory, he was right.

But before he started his cross-breeding experiments, an unusual accident occurred, a human accident that was to prove catastrophic.

To prevent the African queens from escaping, Kerr installed queen excluders at the mouth of each hive. These were small gates with thin slits for openings. The slits were wide enough to allow workers to pass through, but not the queens and drones, which are larger. In order to be absolutely safe, Dr. Kerr put double queen excluders on each hive, built a fence around the hives, and hired a caretaker to watch the colonies.

Then the famous "accident."

The Killer Bees

As the story goes (and we have only Dr. Kerr's word), this is what happened. I quote directly from an interview with him:

Dr. Kerr: *One day, one of the beekeepers, a friend of ours at our college, entered the place to visit the bees. He knew that there were African bees there and he wanted to see them. He found that the bees were losing pollen on the screen, so he decided to open all the hives in order to facilitate the removal of the bees, and prevent the further loss of pollen. After he had done that, he took about one month to inform us, and when we went there we found that 26 hives had swarmed, and these 26 swarms were absolutely out of our control. We tried to find some in the area; we could not find one. It was very difficult, because they could have flown more than ten kilometers by that time. Actually, there was no possibility of finding any of the 26 swarms. So from this moment on—it happened in 1957— begins what we call the Africanization of the Brazilian population of honeybees.*

Author: *Do you know this person who removed the queen excluders and caused the bees to escape?*

Dr. Kerr: *Yes, yes, he was a friend of our group.*

Author: *Have you spoken with him about this, or asked him to explain?*

Dr. Kerr: *Yes, but in our culture when there is not much we can do about something, we don't bother going into it much. You realize, there was nothing that could be done.*

Author: *Did he realize he had made a great mistake?*

Dr. Kerr: *Not at that moment. He realized later on, but since we didn't want him to suffer much, we never spoke very seriously with him about it. We just asked him not to touch our hives anymore.*

Author: *Is it known in this country who he is?*

Dr. Kerr: *To certain groups of beekeepers in Piracicaba, but we don't make propaganda about it.*

The world may therefore never know the identity of the man who perpetrated the most incredible genetic accident in history. We have only Dr. Kerr's word that there is such a man, though he is thoroughly backed up by his colleagues.

It was not through mischief or madness that Dr. Kerr brought the African queens to Brazil. His intent was honorable, and his theory would have worked except for the one unpredictable element that was introduced—man.

It is hard to believe that an experienced beekeeper would knowingly remove queen excluders from 35 hives where African queens were quarantined. The act was deliberate, and bear in mind there were double queen excluders on the hives.

Dr. Kerr's numerous critics believe that measures to prevent the queens from escaping were inadequate, and that the entire quarantine was casual at best. They suggest that the "visiting beekeeper" accident story is merely a cover-up to protect Dr. Kerr.

Nevertheless, Dr. Kerr blames himself for what happened and is bearing a heavy burden.

He said that if he had it to do all over again, he would not have brought the African queens into Brazil, but would have used only the sperm of African drones and created hybrids through artificial insemination.

For several years his work has been dedicated to solving the killer bee problem. To Warwick Kerr, the only solution is through genetics:

In the beginning I felt very badly, and I really suffered very much for having taken part in the introduction of the bee. Then, after 1963, I decided that the best thing would be to dedicate the greatest part of my research to solving the problem.

Emotionally, I felt very badly, I saw some accidents and I didn't want anything bad to happen as an act that I took part in. If I had a chance to start everything all over again, I would choose another way.

In 1957, when they escaped from their sanctuary near São Paulo, the African bees quickly spread north, west, and south. They thrived in the tropical wilds of Brazil, which must have seemed like home to them. They mated with the gentle native Brazilian bees producing extremely aggressive hybrids. The African gene pool was so dominant that they completely took over all the bees in Brazil. And in the wild back country, where there were no Brazilian bees, there are now only Africans.

By 1963 the bees had established themselves in the state and city of Rio de Janeiro. By that time attacks on humans and farm animals were common, and the public became somewhat hysterical because of frequent reports of bee attacks in the press.

In 1965 everyone in Brazil knew about the "killer bees," which had now reached Recife, on the northeast coast of Brazil. In 1969 they moved up the coast to Forteleza and Belém, at the mouth of the Amazon. By 1971 they had crossed the Amazon River and continued their northward movement at a rate of 200 miles a year. Their movement south has been slower because of the more temperate climate, although they are now in Argentina, where they have disrupted the honey industry (Argentina is the world's second leading honey exporter) and caused so much havoc that the Argentine government is considering demanding reparations from Brazil. The killer bees also spread to Paraguay, Uruguay, and Bolivia. They have now reached Surinam and French Guiana to the north and have been officially reported in Venezuela.

Dr. Kerr says the bees are moving north faster because the climate is similar to that of equatorial Africa, where the pure Africans came from. He feels they will eventually reach the United States. But he is hopeful that by that time they will be less aggressive, becoming more gentle as they cross-breed their way through Mexico. Mexico is the leading exporter of honey in the world, and beekeeping is vital to its economy.

It is entirely possible, of course, that exactly the opposite will happen: that the hybrids will remain aggressive. It is also possible that Mexican beekeepers will *want* more aggressive bees to increase their honey production (never underestimate machismo).

Dr. Kerr desperately hopes that genetics will get him out of the problem genetics got him into. "I think we can make a cross between Italians and Africans and select strains for the qualities of production, resistance to disease, and gentleness."

But this theory is valid only in controlled hive areas, such as Dr.

Kerr's 400 hives at the University of São Paulo. One hundred percent control of breeding can be obtained only through artificial insemination. Since killer bees are prone to swarm, most of the colonies are in the wild and therefore beyond human control.

In 1964 Dr. Kerr and his colleagues devised an ingenious scheme to reduce the viciousness of Africanized bees in Brazil. They distributed thousands of virgin Italian queens to beekeepers throughout the country.` The Italian queens mated with African drones in the controlled environment of apiaries. The man who inherited Dr. Kerr's job at the University of São Paulo, Dr. Lionel Gonçalves, has defended this experiment in *The American Bee Journal* of January, 1975:

> *The results of these matings were very good. The productivity of the resultant hybrid bee was almost as high as that of the African bee, but with one great difference: the hybrid bees were gentle. Thus, between 1965 and 1972, we were responsible for the distribution of some 23,000 virgin Italian queens to hundreds of beekeepers. This program was very successful and strongly supported by the beekeepers.*

This view is contradicted by *The Final Report* of the National Academy of Sciences team, which states: "The effort failed at least in part; beekeepers ultimately killed such queens, in spite of their relatively gentle progeny, because they produced less honey than Africanized bees."

In other words, greed had triumphed.

It seems inevitable that, in one form or another, the killer bees will reach the United States. The National Academy of Sciences (NAS) team was gravely concerned and urged immediate action to head off the problem. Several research grants have been funded by the Department of Agriculture and there have been some startling proposals on how to stop the bees, which will be described and discussed in Chapter 9.

The NAS report was published in June, 1972, and it was based on data gathered during November and December of 1971. We now know that the bees have penetrated most of South America with the exception of Chile, which is protected by the formidable natural barrier of the Andes Mountains.

The Killer Bees

The NAS report said that the rate of spread to the south was hindered by the temperate climate, by a lack of trees for abundant nesting sites in much of Argentina and Uruguay, and by management practices by beekeepers.

One frightening aspect to the killer bee story is the fact that the bees have already been in the United States.

In 1960 a scientist at the National Bee Stock Center (run by the USDA) in Baton Rouge, Louisiana, Dr. Stephen Taber III, received semen from five killer bee drones from Dr. Kerr in Brazil. It is illegal to import live, adult honeybees into North America in order to prevent introducing bee diseases. Dr. Kerr and Dr. Taber were experimenting with shipping honeybee semen. Dr. Taber was studying techniques of transporting and storing honeybee semen. He received shipments from many parts of the world to be used to inseminate queens in the United States.

Five of the samples came from Dr. Kerr's African bees in Brazil. This was in 1960, three years after the escape of the original 26 swarms. Two of the queens inseminated with semen from Brazil produced offspring. According to Dr. Taber, after about five generations, he was able to produce 92 percent pure African bees. These offspring were used for breeding experiments. They could not escape because their wings were clipped, but other African hybrids were allowed to fly freely.

Dr. Taber says there are now Africanized bees in the United States, and points out that even before the African bees were brought to Brazil, he experimented with African hybrids at the Madison, Wisconsin, bee laboratory. He said the offspring turned out to be extremely fierce.

While the Kerr-Taber semen experiments were going on in 1960-1961, the Brazilian public had not been informed about the threat of Kerr's Africanized bees. It is probable that Dr. Taber did not realize how aggressive the African bees were, or how quickly they could spread. In Brazil the bees were swarming in the wild and absconding—leaving one nesting place for another. Although there had been many farm animal deaths and attacks on humans, no one anticipated the disasters that were to follow.

At about the same time, Antonio Both, a well-known Brazilian beekeeper (and incidentally our consultant and guide on the NBC documentary), had noticed strange behavior in his hives at Pindamonhangaba, about 100 miles south of Rio de Janeiro.

He says he confronted Dr. Kerr, saying that his own bees had become extremely aggressive, that it required an unusual amount of smoke to handle them, and that they had a nervous flight pattern.

"They're behaving like African bees," Both told Kerr. "Is this possible?"

According to Both, Dr. Kerr admitted that 26 queens he had brought from Africa had escaped. It was, therefore, likely that Antonio Both's bees had become Africanized.

According to Both, it was four years before the public in Brazil learned about the African bee menace. At that time (1961) the bees had not spread very far (it was 1963 before they became firmly established in Rio de Janeiro), but there were frequent attacks on farm animals, and several people had been killed.

The increasing attacks began to concern apiculturist Paulo Nogeiro-Neto, director of the Department of Agriculture for the state of São Paulo. He was aware of the bees' viciousness and considered them a threat to the public.

Nogeiro-Neto was astonished that Dr. Kerr was sending semen from African drones to Dr. Taber in the United States. While Dr. Taber was away on a trip, Nogeiro-Neto contacted Taber's superior, Dr. S. E. McGregor, and urged him to kill the Africanized bees in Baton Rouge. The two nearly-pure African colonies of bees were destroyed, but between 10 and 20 other colonies of Africanized hybrids were *not* destroyed. Worse, they had been allowed to fly freely and to mate with the local bee population. A searing controversy has erupted over the issue of whether or not the bees were destroyed. A prominent bee expert has accused the U.S. Department of Agriculture of deliberately covering up the situation, which could be potentially dangerous to the public.

On September 29, 1965, Dr. Taber wrote a letter to Dr. Kerr in which he mentioned a *Time* magazine article describing the destructiveness of the African bee in Brazil and commented that "from my limited knowledge of genetics, I would guess that it would be impossible for one genetic character or string of characters to 'take over' an entire population [of bees]."

The Killer Bees

The letter triggered a stinging rebuke from Taber's superior, Dr. S. E. McGregor, acting chief of the Agriculture Department's Apiculture Research Branch in Beltsville, Maryland, on the grounds that Taber should not have offered his opinion to an "outsider" on such a controversial matter, especially since legislation proposing a study of the killer bee problem in Brazil was under consideration.

On October 19, 1965, Dr. Taber received a letter from Dr. Kerr, which made the following points:

1. The African bee crosses with black and Italian bees easily. Hybrids vary very much in temper and other characteristics.

2. Brazilian beekeepers were used to very gently bees (black), which were unproductive. Many of them did not like the Italian bees because when crossed with black bees, they offspring were often "mad bees." So they are really upset with the Africans.

3. Africans produce about 70 to 100 percent more honey than Italian bees.

4. About 55 percent of Brazilian beekeepers were happy with the African bees' production, and those beekeepers own 90 percent of the hives.

5. These beekeepers were selecting for fierceness, killing the gentle colonies and leaving the mad ones alive to produce drones.

6. The **Time** *article was instigated by a personal enemy of Dr. Kerr's.*

7. Some Brazilian apiculturists were exaggerating the danger of the African bees in order to obtain more funds from the Brazilian government.

In fairness to Dr. Kerr, it should be repeated that in 1964, a full year before the *Time* article appeared, he had distributed thousands of gentle Italian queens to beekeepers in the attempt to breed the aggressiveness out of the Africans.

Another point worth noting is that Dr. Kerr believes that a Jesuit priest, Father Nedel, who leaked the killer bee story to the American press, was antagonistic toward him on religious and other grounds. It is safe to assume that Father Nedel does not take kindly to man tampering with Nature.

Several scientific articles have defended Dr. Kerr and minimized the potential threat of the Africanized bee to the United States. The most outspoken Kerr partisan is Dr. Roger A. Morse of the Department of Entomology at Cornell University. Dr. Morse wrote a comprehensive article in *Bee World* (Vol. 54, No. 2, 1973), indicating that African bees have been imported into Europe and North America with no harmful effects. He mentions Dr. Taber's experiments with African bee semen in Baton Rouge without comment and goes on to defend the African bee, saying that "some people prefer aggressive bees" and that their temperament can be changed easily through cross-breeding with gentile queens. Dr. Morse blames the "sensationalist" press for the killer bee furor.

The killer bee problem is high complex and the African bee is so adaptable and so unpredictable that it is difficult to make generalizations about it. Many case histories of bee attack victims in Brazil have been documented, and a distinguished scientific committee has verified the bees' rapid spread. Why, then, should we take any chances?

Dr. Marshall Levin, the man responsible for the Department of Agriculture's program to keep the killer bees out of the United States, makes an intriguing point:

There is reason to believe that other shipments of queens have been made to the United States from Africa over the years, but no recognizable effect on our bees has been detected. This lack of impact in the past does not eliminate possible danger from future importations.

The implications are obvious: the African bees never had a chance to get a foothold here in sufficient numbers in a warm climate, as Dr. Kerr's original 26 swarms were able to do in Brazil. However, if a swarm came in on a freighter, or an ambitious beekeeper smuggled in some African queens, they could easily take hold and spread. In addition, there is the danger from the most likely method of entry—the bees could move up through Central America and Mexico into the United States en masse.

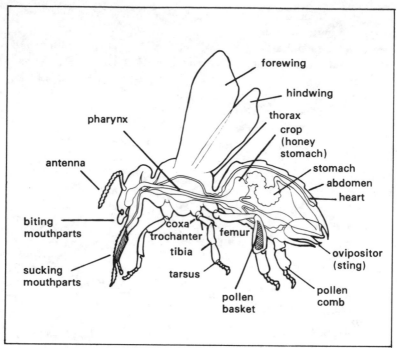

Diagram of a honeybee.

5

Survival of the Fittest

The Killer Bees

"In the survival of favored individuals and races, during the constantly recurring Struggle for Existence, we see a powerful and ever-acting form of Selection."

> Charles Darwin,
> The Origin of Species

"I saw them in the Andes!"

> Antonio Both,
> Brazilian beekeeper

We know how killer bees behave in Brazil, but why these pure Africans and hybrids behave the way they do is a matter of conjecture.

They are clearly highly aggressive and vicious, and most likely developed these traits over a period of thousands of years in Africa, where the natural environment is hostile and the bees are confronted with many predators, including man.

In Africa there is a kind of machismo with regard to bees. The bees that were introduced into Brazil came from Tanzania and Pretoria, South Africa. In both places, it is common for native honey hunters to burn the wild hives, and eat the brood (larvae in the honeycomb) as well as the honey. Over the years the more gentle, docile bees disappeared through natural selection, and only the "fittest" (in this case the most aggressive) bees survived. It was entirely evolutionary. When these vicious bees arrived in Brazil, they were equipped to behave aggressively, to dominate the gentle European bees, and to pass on to their hybrid offspring the traits they had developed in Africa.

To convey how peculiar and threatening the killer bees are, it is necessary to compare them to ordinary honeybees.

Honeybees were not originally native to North or South America, Europe, or Africa. They migrated westward from Asia into Europe and Africa. The temperate climate of southern Europe, combined with advanced beekeeping practices, produced a gentle strain of honeybee. These bees are generally known as Europeans honeybees; the Italian (*mellifera*) and German (*lingustica*) are the most common. They are the gentle varieties known in the United States.

The bees that migrated to Africa had to struggle with a much harsher environment. In order to survive, they had to adapt to a hostile climate and they had to become aggressive. Life was difficult in Africa; food was scarce, and the bees had to be constantly alert and vicious to protect their honey supply. They were quick to attack, and they stayed angry for a much longer time than European honeybees, sometimes for as long as 24 hours. European honeybees attack only in the immediate area of their hive; killer bees have been known to attack and pursue an enemy a mile away. The African bees stayed on the move, and became nomads. Because they reproduce more prolifically than other honeybees, they tend to swarm more. In Africa they learned to nest in whatever shelter was available, such as baobab trees, caves, armadillo shells, and holes in the ground.

They are slightly smaller than standard European bees, though it is difficult for the layman to discern the difference in their appearance. However, it is easy to see the difference in their behavior: they are more unpredictable, adaptable, and aggressive. African bees have a nervous, agitated flight pattern, react more quickly, and fly faster than European bees. They also fly directly into hive entrances rather than landing on entrance boards and walking in.

They are harder workers than Europeans, starting out one-half to two hours earlier in the morning and continuing to work later in the evening, often until darkness. They also forage at lower temperatures and even work in light rain.

Even though African bees are smaller than Europeans, they carry larger nectar loads and can produce up to two times more honey. Dr. Kerr observed that African bees have more sensitive eyesight. He believes this is another result of their genetic adaptation in Africa, where they had to work harder and longer to get honey. This trait is what allows them to start earlier in the morning and work later in the evening than ordinary bees. The fact that they both produce and carry more honey than the somewhat lazier Italians also enables them to survive periods of drought.

From the beekeeper's point of view, the most desirable trait of these bees is their productivity. Many beekeepers are willing to ignore their aggressiveness for this reason.

African queens can lay as many as 5,000 eggs a day (an Italian queen lays 1,500 to 3,000 eggs per day), and they lay eggs throughout the year; hence, the killer bee population explosion. The colonies soon become overcrowded and short of food, at which time the bees swarm and find a new home elsewhere.

Killer bees are believed incapable of adapting to cold weather, and it is thought they could not survive a North American winter. But African bees are so adaptable in other ways, it is possible that if challenged, they could live in cold weather. Antonio Both told me that he had seen Africanized bees in Bolivia's snow-covered Andes Mountains! In Africa, the bees have been sighted at an altitude of 11,000 feet in Ethiopia. And a Polish beekeeper found that African bees could not survive winter in Warsaw, but he discovered that by the third generation they were able to adapt and survive.

Killer bees are notorious wanderers, roving bandits that rob the hives of European bees. Africanized bees also tend to prefer living in the wild, rather than in apiaries. They can live almost anywhere—in hollow trees, hollows in termite nests, in empty boxes, holes in the ground, cracks in cliffs, in empty buildings, tile rooftops, and even in abandoned cars. The countryside in Brazil is full of small colonies of these bees. Bee experts estimate that 90 percent of the killer bees in Brazil live in the "wild." In 1971 Dr. Kerr counted more than 100 Africanized bee nests per square kilometer in the savanna area of north-central Brazil! This makes it extremely difficult (if not impossible) to control killer bees through genetics.

Killer bees have learned to survive under the most adverse conditions. They rarely die inside a hive from lack of food or water. Their survival instinct is such that they will abscond and migrate until they either find suitable conditions or die. An absconding swarm will not leave without a queen. Therefore, one way of preventing swarming is to clip the wings of the queen so she cannot fly.

Killer bees will often take over the hives of Italian colonies in apiaries. A small swarm of killer bees will settle on a hive, usually under the edge of the lid or under the bottom board, enter the hive, sometimes at night, and kill the Italian queen. The workers and drones in the hive accept the new African queen, and thus the killer bees take over the hive.

In Curitiba I actually saw a killer bee swarm try to take over an Italian hive. We were with Dr. Paul Sommer, Secretary of Agriculture in the state of Paraná. As we were filming his hives in a rural apiary, the killer bee swarm flew to the ground just under the front of the hive. The bees lay on the grass like a huge dark mat. Suddenly a band of workers and the queen flew to the lid; they had launched their attack. Dr. Sommer quickly caught the African queen and killed it. But this was a classic example of how killer bees take over gentle hives.

We had gone to Curitiba at the suggestion of Dr. Kerr to observe the more "gentle" Africanized bees in southern Brazil, where the climate is temperate and beekeeping is more sophisticated than in the north. There we had contacted Dr. Sommer and driven out to one of his apiaries on a farm 50 miles south of Curitiba.

Dr. Sommer believes the killer bees will reach the United States "in fewer years than expected," and that when they do, they will be "the aggressive type of northern Brazil."

He told us that killer bees have drastically reduced the number of commercial beekeepers in Paraná, and virtually wiped out hobbyists. He said it is impossible to keep the bees near animals because they are so ferocious that they will attack on the slightest provocation and sometimes their attacks are entirely unprovoked. According to Dr. Sommer, in 1965, a peak year for the killer bee, commercial beekeeping in southern Brazil was wiped out and beekeepers had to start all over again and develop new systems of bee management. They could no longer keep their hives close together, as they had in the past; the hives had to be separated by about 10 yards because adjacent hives will group together for an attack. A typical apiary before killer bees arrived contained about 150 hives; now, because the bees are so vicious and difficult to manage, no more than 40 hives are feasible, and these cannot be kept near farm animals.

Dr. Sommer's bees were far from gentle, as advertised, and he had to use heavy doses of smoke to control them. Perhaps the bees in southern Brazil are not as fierce as those in the north, but they are certainly far from gentle.

Killer bees swarm to reproduce when the hive or nest becomes overcrowded and they need *lebensraum*. The swarms are enormous, containing anywhere from 40,000 to 60,000 bees, and their dominant trait is the viciousness with which they attack animals and people with little or no provocation.

The individual stings of killer bees are not lethal; what makes these bees so deadly is that they attack in such great numbers. Up to 40,000 enraged bees will all pursue an enemy at the same time. It takes only 50 to 100 stings to kill the average person (of course, one sting can be fatal if the person is allergic to bee stings).

The NAS report, which is objective and dispassionate, says that "Brazilian bees differ dramatically from other races in their great sensitivity to colony disturbance, their ability to communicate alarm within and between colonies, and their capacity to respond quickly by massive attack on intruders."

The Killer Bees

Here it is necessary to explain an important term, *alarm pheromone*. This is the chemical released by bees when they are threatened: it is a call to attack. Most experts believe that killer bees release alarm pheromones more quickly than other bees, and that they are more sensitive to the smell; thus they attack more quickly and in greater numbers. The NAS report explains the phenomenon this way:

> *The mechanisms (to respond quickly by massive attack) are not clear, but could involve the release of greater quantities of alarm pheromones; the different behavior in pheromone release, e.g. release at the hive entrance instead of in the air; an enhanced responsiveness to alarm pheromones; increased use of visual and auditory signals around the victim; or some combination of the above factors.*

> *The slightest disturbance at or near the hive entrance...can set off a chain reaction that 'EXPLODES' within seconds; whole apiaries may go out of control. Hundreds of bees become airborne and pursue and sting any animals or people within 100 meters of the apiary. The committee was greatly impressed by the vigor and duration of such intensive aggressive behavior in northern Brazil, where some committee members were stung severely, even though they anticipated the problem by wearing protective gear, and by massively smoking the hives.*

The committee also observed that "disturbed bees pursue a person or animal that has been stung for distances far greater than is usual for European bees; in tests by the committee, pursuit for at least one kilometer was recorded." In Recife killer bees attacked our documentary team for more than two hours. These same bees stung villagers as far as one mile away for several hours, long into the night.

Killer bees are totally unpredictable. One beekeeper told the NAS team that the bees are particularly aggressive during a honey flow; another said their aggressiveness increased when there was a scarcity of food. Some beekeepers reported bees more vicious in hot weather, others in cool weather; still others claimed the bees became nastier in high humidity. All agreed on one point: aggressiveness is variable, and a colony that is difficult to handle one day may be relatively docile another day.

The NAS Committee had several experiences similar to ours in Recife, but one in particular stands out. It was in Taquara, Rio Grande do Sul, in southern Brazil, where killer bees are not supposed to be that aggressive.

A particularly dangerous attribute of Brazilian bees [hybrids resulting from cross-breeding between Africans and Europeans] is their aggressiveness after slight jarring or vibration of the hive. A Brazilian colony judged to be only moderately aggressive...was extremely aggressive when tested after the hive had been inadvertently jarred. The disturbance of the hive was slight, but the test-leather (black leather ball) received 92 stings in only 5 seconds!

The person conducting the test left immediately instead of waiting for the prescribed 30 seconds, and the angry bees followed the leather (and the person carrying it) for over a kilometer!

Here's how the committee describes the killer bee:

*The following characteristics of the Brazilian honeybee are **advantageous** for the reasons stated:*

Flight of workers—bees work long hours, work in the cold and carry large loads.

Productivity—appears to be high.

Development cycle—populations increase rapidly.

*The following characteristics are **disadvantageous**:*

Seasonal cycle—adapt poorly to winter.

Killing queens—occurs when there are disturbances, such as jarring of the hive.

The Killer Bees

Nest locations—large feral (wild) populations form in natural nesting sites.

Absconding and swarming—abscond and swarm excessively.

Stinging—excessive aggressiveness and keen ability to communicate alarm requires that hives be dispersed.

Robbing—do so excessively.

Primarily because of the last four qualities of the Brazilian bee listed above, they are supplanting the European races in apiaries.

The NAS team was obviously quite impressed by the threat of killer bees. And the committee's summary is ominous:

A strain of honeybee not yet present in North America seems likely to enter that continent from the south, if its spread is neither hindered nor helped through human agencies. This strain, now rapidly extending its range in South America, has both objectionable and dangerous attributes. Because of its unprovoked mass stinging and because of frequent swarming and absconding, the Brazilian bee is dangerous to people and animals and is difficult to manage. It has already brought about drastic changes in the beekeeping industry in the areas it occupies in South America.

*To control the northward spread of this bee will probably require action on the Central American isthmus, perhaps within the next four to six years—action, the nature of which will depend on the results of experimental work not yet begun. **There is no known geographic or climatic barrier that will prevent the spread of the Brazilian bee into North America.** In South America it now ranges from the equator to about 34 degrees S, indicating that it could well survive throughout Mexico and in the southern United States. Southward spread in South America is now slow, but to the north the area of infestation is moving about 200 miles a year and has crossed the Amazon. Still further, the population in the north is the most aggressive found by the Committee in its survey.*

In view of the above, the Committee feels that it is essential to do whatever can be done to minimize the likelihood of this bee moving into North America.

Several research projects, funded by the U.S. Department of Agriculture, are now under way. These and other plans of action to keep the bees out of the United States will be discussed in Chapter 9. Meanwhile, the killer bees continue to move north.

One of the most mysterious occurrences of the killer bee adventure took place before I went to Brazil. It began in San Diego, California, and ended at the Army's Chemical-Biological Warfare Center at Edgewood Arsenal in Maryland. I had heard that the military was experimenting with killer bee venom but I had no idea why. My first contact was with a U.S. Navy chemist, Dr. William Shipman, at the Naval Underseas Center in San Diego.

Dr. Shipmen met me in his laboratory. He is a tall, thin, distinguished-looking man with gray hair and steel-rimmed glasses, probably in his mid-fifties. He was immediately friendly and open— unusual at any military base, but particularly a research center. Dr. Shipman is a bee hobbyist. He has been studying killer bee venom as part of a joint Army-Navy program to protect field troops from venomous animals and insects. What he told me was quite frightening:

We're looking at the venom problems of all venomous creatures our troops can encounter anywhere in the world to develop antivenins and protective mechanisms.

We have looked at cobras, sea snakes, rattlesnakes, spiders, and, of course, honeybees. In conjunction with my study of honeybee venom, I obtained some venom from Brazil, venom from the Africanized bees of Brazil.

We are hoping to develop an antivenin that is effective against more than one species. This is our primary target.

Dr. Shipman said he was working closely with Major (now Colonel) James Vick, who was chief of neurophysiology at

Edgewood Arsenal. He said that he separated the venom into its components and Vick tested it pharmacologically on research animals:

> *Together we have found that there are many differences in the components of the venom. Some of the components affect the nerves. We call it a **neurotoxin**, that is, a toxin that attacks the nerves and does nerve damage. **This component is found in the Africanized bee and not in the bees of the United States.***
>
> *Jim has found that the venom is approximately twice as toxic as the venom we're accustomed to seeing in the United States.*
>
> *When you combine increased toxicity of the venom and increased aggressiveness of the bee, you have a very undesirable combination.*

I was stunned by the implications of what Dr. Shipman had just recited in an offhand manner: that killer bee venom is twice as toxic as ordinary bee venom and attacks the nervous system. I realized immediately that his was *new* information, that it had not been reported in scientific journals yet, and had not been mentioned by any of the bee experts I had interviewed. Was it possible it was being kept from the public for fear of panicking people?

Dr. Shipman considers the killer bee a real and constant threat to any U.S. troops that may be operating in Central or South America. He said his experiments are stalled because he cannot get any more killer bee venom, despite the fact that both he and Colonel Vick have written Dr. Kerr several times requesting it. Three of his letters to Dr. Kerr have gone unanswered. Kerr's resistance began after he learned of the discovery that Africanized bee venom is more toxic than European bee venom.

This discovery is where Colonel Vick comes in.

Edgewood Arsenal is an ominous place. It was one of the Army's major research centers for testing chemical-biological warfare agents; it was also a major chemical warfare production center. Now that the Army is no longer in the CBW business, the facilities have been turned over to medical research.

Colonel Vick is a young, good-looking man and is extremely open and cooperative. I found it hard to believe I was in one of the Army's most secret places as this friendly officer showed me around, opening doors, and letting me film his experiments without restrictions. Of course, none of this work was classified and I'm sure that experiments with bee venom are not very high on the Army's priority list.

Colonel Vick took me for a tour of his lab. He was experimenting with monkeys, mice, and dogs (beagles bred specifically for medical research). If you've ever been in the monkey room of a research center, you know that the smell is unbearable and that the monkeys often grab at you from their cages. One large rhesus monkey there had electrodes implanted in his brain to measure the effects of bee venom on brainwave activity; but the bulk of the research used mice in what was called "a mouse assay test." In this test the mice are injected with bee venom of increasing dosages on a scale of one to ten, until a lethal dose is achieved.

"We've found Brazilian bee venom to be at least twice as toxic as American bee venom," Colonel Vick told me. "It kills experimental animals at a dose one-half that required of American bee venom. The Brazilian bee is obviously producing either a superpotent venom, or its components are more powerful in their actions."

Just how powerful one of these components is, I saw graphically displayed. Colonel Vick prepared a large 25-pound rhesus monkey for an unusual experiment. He was going to test an isolated component of killer bee venom called Phospholipase A.

"This is the substance common to snake venom such as cobra venom, coral snake venom—even rattlesnakes have a certain degree of Phospholipase A in them," he explained. "It's not unique to bee venom itself, or even to African bee venom. It is a substance found in all the toxic materials of nature."

Colonel Vick said Phospholipase A is probably the component that causes breathing difficulties, the neurotoxin.

The rhesus monkey lay spread-eagle, face up, on an operating table. He was strapped down and had electrodes attached to measure his heart rate, respiration, and blood pressure, and to give an electrocardiogram (EKG) reading. All these measurements would be printed out on a graph. Colonel Vick and his lab assistant surgically implanted an arterial catheter to inject the killer bee toxin, Phospholipase A.

Survival of the Fittest

Colonel Vick began injecting the equivalent of five bee stings directly into the monkey's vein through the catheter. He provided a running commentary as he worked:

Blood pressure's falling. That's four, the equivalent of four bee stings. Okay. The last is going in. That's five.

He then flushed the catheter to make sure all the toxin went into the monkey and peered over at the graph. The needles were moving rapidly.

The blood pressure is falling tremendously. Respiration is very erratic. The heart seems to be beating rather regularly, so it appears as though what we suspected is true: we're getting a purely respiratory effect. As a matter of fact . . . [His voice trailed off and he looked worried. He nervously looked at the graph, then at the monkey, which was having difficulty breathing.]

We have a real problem. We'll have to go on artificial respiration now. [The colonel hooked the monkey to a respirator and fastened the oxygen mask to its face.]

Okay. We're giving him artificial respiration due to the fact that he's not able to breathe on his own.

So it appears as though what we suspected is really true, that the Phospholipase A from the Brazilian honeybee is the culprit that causes the complete arrest of breathing. With the equivalent of five bee stings, this animal went into respiratory paralysis and is now having to be supported on artificial respiration; elsewise, he would have died several moments ago. With artificial respiration, the animal should go on to live for a prolonged period of time and hopefully he'll recover.

I was quite surprised at what had just happened and remembered that in the days of CBW research no animals left Edgewood Arsenal alive. Although I was upset at the condition of the monkey, the colonel and his lab assistant were casual about it. I asked Colonel Vick to explain the significance of what had just happened.

This Phospholipase A is about twice as powerful as that which comes from the typical American honeybee, so there's a definite difference in its ability to cause respiratory paralysis. In very basic terms, it appears that if you were stung by the Brazilian honeybee, your chances of having breathing difficulites would be much greater than if you were stung by the typical honeybee.

I asked if it was unusual for the equivalent of five bee stings to cause such a severe reaction in the monkey.

"Yes, it certainly is," Colonel Vick explained. He seemed slightly embarrassed:

We're rather surprised because five bee stings usually will cause dramatic changes in blood pressure and breathing, yet not kill. This is rather dramatic.

We're really seeing the effect of this superpotent component of Brazilian honeybee venom on the breathing mechanism. Of course, we've suspected this for some time, but this is the first time we've been able to verify it. This is the first time we have tested this particular component of the bee venom.

The monkey is about one-tenth the size of the average human being—or we're about ten times as big as he is—so the equivalent amount of venom for us to have this same effect would be 50 stings. So it's very probable that the 50 stings that might be incurred from an actual swarm of Brazilian bees might produce the respiratory paralysis, or the difficulties in breathing. There's no way of telling whether the individual would just have trouble breathing, but from this data, it would certainly indicate that there would be a serious problem.

The monkey died two hours later.

The Killer Bees

Colonel Vick would like to develop an antitoxin or an antivenin to immunize troops that might come into contact with "these superpotent bees." His work is being held up, however, because he cannot get any more killer bee venom.

In Brazil, I was able to confirm Colonel Vick's findings with another researcher. When I was in Curitiba pondering the fact that Dr. Paulo Sommer's southern bees were not as gentle as they were supposed to be, I decided to look up another contact. Dr. Hans Jakobi, a professor of biology at the University of Paraná. Serendipity led me to Dr. Jakobi; I really didn't know what to expect from him or how he could help me, but on an impulse dropped in to see him. When I reached his cluttered laboratory in an old stone building that sits in the heart of Curitiba, I found a rotund, beaming man in his fifties. Balding, bespectacled, and jolly, he was a Kris Kringle of a man, by far the friendliest person I met in Brazil. As it turned out, he had been studying the killer bee for 15 years. Dr. Jakakobi and his son Paulo, a medical student at the university, were looking into the physiopathology of bee attack victims; that is, they were examining the pathological effects of the venom's toxicity.

Dr. Jakobi had been testing the killer bee venom on frogs. By injecting the venom into isolated frog hearts (kept alive in a saline-alcohol solution), he discovered that the venom's heart-blocking action was much more powerful than that of European bee venom.

After many experiments, he concluded that killer bee venom is much more toxic than European bee venom, but he has not yet determined how much more potent it is. Since the research is still going on, the data are incomplete, but on the basis of completed experiments, he said that if a human being, say a man weighing 150 pounds, was stung more than 30 times, it would be very dangerous and probably fatal.

A Zulu honey-hunter taking honey from a hive of African bees nesting in a Baobob tree in south Africa. For thousands of years natives have robbed the hives of African bees for honey. Over the years only the fierce and aggressive bees have survived.

A pure African bee forages for honey in south Africa, where they became aggressive in order to survive. Because they are harder workers than European bees, they were taken to Brazil to increase honey production.

African queens can lay up to 5,000 eggs a day. Even when they cross-breed with gentle bees, the off-spring are aggressive, Africanized hybrids.

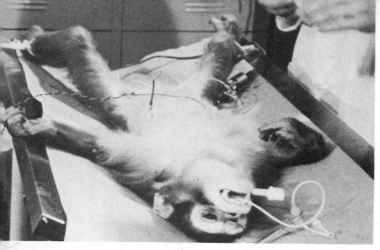

This rhesus monkey is being injected with bee venom at the U.S. Army's former chemical-biological warfare center at Edgewood, Maryland. Researchers here discovered that killer bee venom is twice as toxic as the venom of European bees, common in the United States.

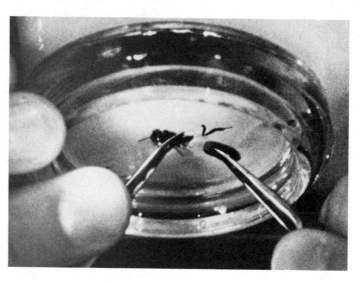

Dissecting a sample bee is the first step in a new method of identifying killer bees by computer. This is at the University of California, at Berkeley, where Dr. Howell Daly, an entomologist, developed the new technique. The research project is funded by the U.S. Department of Agriculture.

The Africanized hybrids going and coming to their hive in the daily work routine. They forage for long hours.

The bee with the white dot is a pure African queen that is being used in genetic experiments at the University of São Paulo in Ribeirao Preto, Dr. Kerr's colleagues are attempting to produce a honeybee which is more gentle than Africans, while retaining the capacity for hard work and greater honey production.

Dr. Warwick Kerr explains a point to his class in the Department of Genetics at the University of São Paulo.

This is called a "queen excluder." It prevents queens and drones, which are larger than worker bees from leaving the hive. Queen excluders similar to this one were removed from the quarantined hives that Dr. Kerr had established in 1957. Twenty-six African queens and their swarms thus escaped, and have since taken over all of South America.

This is a swarm of killer bees and hive in a mango tree near Recife. There are about 40,000 bees in this swarm, which is next to a housing development and an elementary school. A falling mango or tree branch could incite the bees to attack.

In Recife, a colony of killer bees has nested in the ear of this statue of Joaquim Nabuco, who freed the slaves in Brazil in 1850. The statue is located in the middle of a busy plaza in downtown Recife.

While the NBC crew was filming a vicious hive in Recife, a curious chicken got too close. The bees repeatedly stung the chicken, killing it within a few minutes. The white spots are stingers.

Firemen in Recife use butane torches to destroy a colony of killer bees nesting in a roof. The specially equipped and trained "bee squad" average four calls a day to destroy killer bees.

Our film crew explored the jungle in the Recife area in order to find the Africanized hybrids living in the wilds.

Our NBC film crew in full protective gear amidst the test hives of Recife.

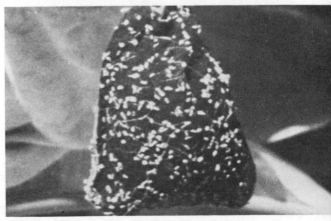

This black jeweler's pouch was dangled at the mouth of a hive of killer bees near Recife in an "aggressiveness test." The pouch took more than 500 stings in less than two minutes. Each dot is a stinger embedded in the pouch; bees die when they sting.

In one of the more spectacular attacks, on September 16, 1965, killer bees invaded the main business section, Rio Branco, in downtown Rio de Janeiro. Rio Branco is the center of Rio's movie district, similar to Times Square in New York. The bees stung more than 60 people, sending them running frantically in all directions. The bees were finally dispersed with pesticides.

Mexico is the leading honey exporter in the world. Honey is vital to the Mexican economy, and Mexicans like aggressive bees: they produce more honey, and they protect their hives from intruders and robbers. Also, the challenge of handling aggressive bees seems to appeal to the Latin beekeepers.

One of our South American beekeeper guides wears the protective helmet and veil.

A group of South American beekeepers smoke a hive in order to calm the aggressive bees enough that they can work in the hives.

Bee experts in Brazil place their faith in genetics to solve the killer bee problem. By artificial insemination of African queens, they hope to produce a more gentle bee. This is feasible in a controlled environment, but not in the wild, where most killer bees live.

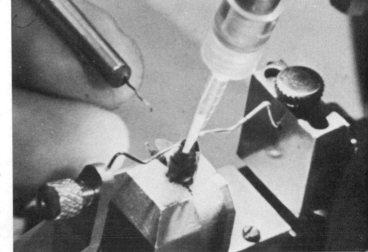

Dec. 5, 1973—Firemen use flaming butane torches to destroy a colony of killer bees which attacked a funeral procession in Rio's Caju Cemetery. The bees became enraged when the funeral director threw a handful of sand at them. The vicious bees attacked nearly 300 people in the cemetery.

6

The Situation in Brazil
Living with Killer Bees

"Call in thy deaths's head there: tie up thy fears."

George Herbert

As the killer bees moved northward in Brazil, they became nastier, possibly because the hot, humid equatorial north of Brazil is more like their native Tanzania and South Africa. Scientists are not sure whether the increased viciousness is due to the weather or some genetic change in the bees. Since we were searching for aggressive bees, our guide recommended that we go to Racife, the site of several recent killer bee attacks.

Recife, like most towns and cities in Brazil, has learned to live with killer bees. They are so much a part of everyday life that people ignore them, unless they are attacked. In the heart of Recife there is an impressive statue honoring one of Brazil's great heroes, Joaquím Nabuco. Now the statue's left ear provides a home for a nest of killer bees.

The bees have been living in the statue's ear since 1968; they have not attacked anybody—yet. The reason is that the swarm is too small and is not secure; also, it is too high to be bothered by people. The statue is in the middle of a small park in Recife; shoeshine boys casually lounge around it as the bees fly in and out of the statue's ear, and strollers walk directly under the bees without even glancing at the swarm.

The Killer Bees

Next, we drove five miles to a suburb of Recife, the small town of Olinda, one of the oldest settlements in Brazil. It was founded in 1537 and has beautifully preserved examples of 16th-century colonial architecture. We had heard there was a large swarm of killer bees in a mango grove behind the church and convent of São Francisco.

The mother superior, a charming and cheerful lady, showed us the abandoned hives behind the church, where they had produced honey for the convent—that is, before killer bees arrived in Recife. When the bees became Africanized, they were too aggressive to manage, so the sisters gave up beekeeping. The only reminder of that activity is a sinister swarm of killer bees hanging in a mango tree halfway down the side of a hill by the church.

We awkwardly set up our tripod on the side of the hill, moving slowly and carefully, afraid that we might jostle the tree and anger the bees. While we were taking pictures, a mango dropped from the tree and we froze. Killer bees are often provoked by vibrations; a falling mango could easily incite the swarm. Fortunately, the mango did not hit the bees, so we continued taking pictures, gingerly. There were at least 40,000 bees in the colony. The hive was ominous, just hanging there, like a time bomb that could explode any second. We could hear a faint humming sound from the colony, and we saw several workers, or sentries, darting in and out of the tree. It was most disturbing to realize that the swarm was only a few hundred yards from a housing development and an elementary school. We saw little children playing nearby, unaware that, hidden in the mango grove, was a colony of killer bees. If a falling mango hit the bees, or if a limb broke, or even if a strong wind stirred up the colony, the killer bees, thousands of them, could attack the schoolchildren. Having experienced the ferocity of killer bees, the thought made me shudder.

We had heard that recently eight people in Recife had been attacked by killer bees and hospitalized. The local fire department reportedly had responded to the call and killed the bees with a flamethrower.

We tracked down the site of the attack; it was on a quiet residential street in Recife, at the home of 49-year-old Guermercino d'Almeida. Two months earlier he had noticed a swarm of bees flying into the open top drawer of an old table in his backyard. Afraid to bother the colony, d'Almeida went on vacation and soon forgot about it. Just a few days before our arrival in Recife, he was gardening in his backyard, unmindful of the swarm of bees still living in the old abandoned table. While d'Almeida was raking and sweeping near the table, a bee stung him on the back of the neck. He swatted at it, and more bees came. Then more. And more. He hit at the bees and ran, screaming for help. The bees stung him on his face, neck, arms, back, and all over his head, even inside his ears.

"I had bees in my ears and I ran, yelling. I was terrified," he said. "I was taking a bee out of my ear when others fell on top of me, on my hair, stinging."

D'Almeida collected tropical birds and was proud of his expensive collection. He displayed them in cages by the side of his house. During the bee attack, he ran frantically past the caged birds.

"The bees covered the birds, the parrot, the dogs, everything. I ran terrified, yelling. I jumped over the wall and fell on the street. The bees were all over me, on the birds, on the dogs. I screamed for help, and that's all I remember. The sensation was horrible, really horrible. I thought it was the end."

D'Almeida was stung unconscious. Some neighbors helped him and called an ambulance. Besides d'Almeida, the vicious bees stung his five-year-old daughter and six neighbors. D'Almeida remained in the hospital near death for 15 hours. He was given massive injections of adrenaline and antihistamine tablets. He was released the next day; the others had been treated in the hospital emergency room and were released the day of the attack.

D'Almeida was lucky to survive. Prompt medical attention saved his life. Unfortunately, that was the end of his tropical bird collection. The bees had killed one rare parrot, seven other exotic tropical birds, and d'Almeida's two fox terriers.

Killer bees attacks are so common in Recife that the fire department (called the *departimento de bombeiros*) has a bee squad, specifically trained and equipped to destroy swarms of bees nesting in rooftops or in empty buildings. Every major city and most small towns in Brazil have such squads.

Many houses in Recife have tile roofs, and killer bees often colonize on rooftops, under the tiles. The owner of one such house, Dr. Mario Baptista, a prominent lawyer in Recife, did not know that a colony of killer bees was living in his roof until a single bee stung him on the forehead.

The Killer Bees

His face and neck became swollen, he developed a very high fever, and his eyes were swollen shut. He told me that the pain was unbearable. It turned out that Dr. Baptista was allergic to bee stings. Fortunately, his neighbor was a doctor and treated him quickly, thus saving his life. The neighbor then called the *bombeiros*.

The men of the bee squad wear heavy protective clothing: very thick coveralls, boots, thick leather gloves, and wire mesh netting over their faces. The netting is stiff so it will not press against their faces when they're working. They also wear steel helmets. *Bombeiros* usually kill bees by burning them, using butane torches, which are actually flamethrowers. They burn the bees flying in and out of the rooftop; as more bees rush out to attack, they meet the same fate. The firemen then remove the tiles from the roof and burn the entire area where the bees have been nesting. After killing the bees with the torches, they burn the honeycomb, then scoop it out and destroy the eggs, or larvae.

During January, 1975, the Recife Fire Department's special bee squad was called 97 times. The September before, it was called 155 times. Year round, it averages four calls a day to destroy colonies of killer bees. A fireman in Fortaleza, a city to the northwest of Recife near the equator, said their men often get as many as 20 calls a day.

Most of the time the bee squads are able to destroy killer bees with the flamethrowers, but occasionally they must use strong pesticides, or a combination of both. Of course, once the bees have launched an attack, it is almost impossible to calm them down. In Fortaleza in the tropical region of northern Brazil, where killer bee attacks seem to be more frequent and more vicious, there were 964 incidents involving killer bees in 1970. In one attack the son-in-law of the Secretary of Agriculture for the state was killed. He was a young doctor, who was spending a weekend at a farm with his children. As he was walking with them in a pasture next to some woods, he was attacked and killed by Africanized bees. In a desperate move, the distraught Minister of Agriculture contacted Antonio Both and urged him to help in the battle against killer bees. Both recommended poisoning the honey in the hives with venom. The method proved successful, killing thousands of hives in apiaries, and the next year, 1971, there were only 69 killer bee incidents in Fortaleza. These figures, of course, include only those incidents reported to the fire departments. Countless other attacks in the countryside go unreported, and 90 percent of all killer bees live in the wild back country of Brazil.

In Recife, while we were talking about the seriousness of the killer bee threat in Brazil, Antonio Both made some ominous predictions. He said that Africanized bees would wipe out the beekeeping industry as we know it in the United States. He also pointed out that Africanized bees cannot be used for crop pollination, the most important use for bees in the United States. According to Both, the bees along the coastal areas of Brazil, in both the north and the south, are African hybrids. But in the dense interior of the country the bees' characteristics are pure African, because they have not successively mated with existing bee populations.

Antonio Both has been working on the killer bee problem for 16 years, ever since he confronted Dr. Kerr in 1961. Though he has become something of a celebrity, he remains unaffected, still a man of the soil. He served as a consultant for the National Academy of Sciences team which went to Brazil in 1971 to determine what impact killer bees will have on the United States, if and when they arrive. Later he was hired as a consultant by *National Geographic* for its article on killer bees in the issue of April, 1976.

I considered it vital to our expedition to have someone of Both's experience and knowledge along, so I was quite upset one night when he failed to meet us in Rio de Janeiro at the appointed time. He has no telephone, so I had sent several telegrams to his home, each stressing our urgent need for his services. Finally, after my third *batida* (a potent Brazilian drink made with fresh limes, sugar, ice, and Pitu, a devastating sugarcane whisky), I had given up and was resigned to carry on without him when I was called to the telephone. It was Antonio Both, acting as though nothing had happened and asking when we wanted to meet him. I wanted to say, "Immediately," but asked him how soon he could come to Rio. He said he had taken a little vacation to work his apiary in Pernambuco. He was now home in Pindamonhangaba, about three hours south of Rio. He would take a bus and meet me at the Copacabaña Palace Hotel at about midnight.

The Killer Bees

It was midnight *en punto* when a tall gangling man walked into the bar, asking for "Señor Poater."

"Señor Both?" I asked.

"*Si*," he replied.

"*Con mucho gusto, senŏr,*" I said.

It was Spanish, but little matter, he understood anyway. I grabbed his hand enthusiastically, but felt something odd. I looked at his right hand and noticed that his right forefinger was missing. Later on, during the trip, he was notified that his oldest son had lost *his* right forefinger while using an electric saw. Antonio did not seem bothered by that; in fact, he seemed to glow a little with pride. He considered the missing right forefinger a family trait that he had now passed on to his son.

As we talked for several hours I realized how much Antonio knew about bees. It seemed incredible, but he had become virtually immune to bee stings and understood bees' behavior so well that he could actually lead a swarm around. Of course any experienced beekeeper can do that, but Antonio was absolutely unafraid of killer bees. Later, he would regret being so casual when we were attacked by an extremely vicious colony.

In Recife, after traveling with Antonio for about a week, when we were bone tired and the search for the killer bee had totally captured our imaginations, I sat talking with him on the patio of the Hotel Miramar when something occurred to me. Antonio is very tall and very thin. He has gray-black hair worn in a brush cut. His face is angular, and he wears very thick, large round glasses. His eyesight is poor and the thick glasses magnify his eyes, which are green, about ten times. He has huge ears that stick out, and combined with his crew cut and his tendency to stare at you when he's talking (or listening), it suddenly struck me—Antonio Both looked like a bee!

That thought was to provide much comic relief during the rest of the trip.

Dr. Hans Jakobi has been keeping track of killer bee incidents for 15 years in Curitiba, where more than 100 bee attacks a month occur during the hot summer months. Professor Jakobi told me of an unusual killer bee attack that involved him personally. In the summer of 1967 he was taking 40 of his students on an ecological field trip to an island in the Bay of Paraná. They had rented a large boat, and four hours out from Curitiba, when they were about to anchor about 100 yards from the beach, a swarm of killer bees attacked the boat. Fifteen girls were stung and one girl almost killed. She was allergic to bee stings. Fortunately Dr. Jakobi was carrying an emergency bee-sting kit. He gave the girl an injection of adrenaline and some antihistamine tablets, and these saved her life.

Dr. Jakobi also told me the story of an acquaintance who was attacked by killer bees while walking home from a tavern one evening after having had too much to drink. As he was walking, he was whistling, chewing pampas grass, and throwing small rocks into the underbrush. Apparently he hit a nest of killer bees, which became irritated and attacked him. He started running and dove into a deep pond, holding his breath, swimming underwater as far as he could to escape the attacking bees.

When he came up for air, the bees were hovering over the exact spot, and continued to attack him, covering his head and face. He screamed and gasped for air, swallowing some bees that had flown into his mouth. The killer bees had actually tracked him while he was swimming underwater. The man's body was found the next morning, floating face down in the pond, bloated from the water. The face was hideously swollen from the hundreds of bee stings—so much so that his eyes were mere slits and his head the size of a watermelon.

It was not determined whether he had died from the toxic affect of the bee stings, from sheer terror which could have caused a heart attack, or from drowning.

Dr. Jakobi had learned the details from the fire department and a witness who had seen the attack, but could do nothing to help. It happened just 30 miles outside of Curitiba.

Killer bees have driven virtually all Brazilian hobbyists out of business. It is true that in southern Brazil, where beekeeping has been refined by Europeans (particularly the Germans), beekeepers have learned to manage the Africanized bee and to take advantage of its increased honey production. They have been able to accomplish this partly because of the temperate climate and genetics, and partly because of the sophisticated bee-management techniques practiced there. Nevertheless, almost all the beekeepers interviewed by the NAS team agreed that aggressiveness is the most undesirable trait of the Afro-Brazilian honeybee.

The Killer Bees

As the original handful of African bees multiplied into millions of swarms of ferocious guerilla-like bands, the wild strains disrupted the hives and honey-gathering activities of the more tame European bees already in Brazil. Brazil once exported honey, but proliferation of the African bees at first caused its honey output to drop by 90 percent. It became necessary for the former exporting country to become an importer of honey. (This situation prompted the manufacture of artificial honey laced with glucose.)

Essentially, the pattern of Africanization of bees in southern Brazil is this: The killer bees arrive and virtually wipe out commercial and amateur beekeeping. Then, several years later, commercial beekeepers start all over again and end up producing more honey with fewer bees. At least this is the case with Dr. Paulo Sommer in Curitiba, and is also true of some professional beekeepers in Florianópolis and other southern cities. But it is not true in northern Brazil, where the climate is hotter and the bees more aggressive.

Dr. Orly Taylor of the University of Kansas has a USDA grant to try to pinpoint the northward progress of the killer bee. He has verified that the bees have reached French Guiana and Surinam. Dr. Taylor has spent a great deal of time in both southern and northern Brazil and seems to me an objective observer without vested interests.

He reports that in southern Brazil the initial effect of the Africanized bee was to depress honey and wax production. But within five to ten years, honey and wax production increased to higher levels than achieved previously. This is because the beekeepers who stayed in business adopted appropriate beekeeping techniques, and perhaps also because the bees' behavioral traits were modified through intensive, controlled cross-breeding in apiaries with gentle Italian bees. This can be accomplished under controlled circumstances; the problem is that most of the killer bees live in the wild, where it is impossible to control genetics.

Dr. Taylor concluded that while the short-term effects of the introduction of African bees appear severe, the long-term effects seem to be beneficial. However, he pointed out that the opportunities to modify bee behavior through genetic manipulation are limited in northern South America and Central America. He said that beekeeping is less intensive there and thus, as large wild populations of Africanized bees move into the area, the dilution effect will be very slight. He believes that "genetic dilution without intensive selection will not be sufficient to result in substantial modification of the Africanized bees as they move northward."

Dr. Taylor maintains:

Amateur beekeepers usually find these bees too aggressive to handle. Three beekeepers we interviewed had abandoned or destroyed their colonies, and in one location (Rio Branco, Brazil) a cooperative operation involving 50 beekeepers was abandoned shortly after the Africanized bee arrived. We did not meet any beekeeper who adapted to the bee and know of only one commercial beekeeper who is keeping bees in northern Brazil.

Of course this is Dr. Taylor's experience only. Brazil is a large country. I found a cooperative in Recife (there are only ten commercial beekeepers there) where the beekeepers are learning to deal with Africanized bees. They wear heavy protective clothing, and disperse the hives, keeping them far away from people and farm animals. They also use heavy smokers to calm the bees, making them easier to handle. Although these beekeepers are not technically advanced, Dr. Lionel Gonçalves (a colleague of Dr. Kerr's) reports that in 1972 they were able to export 800 tons of honey to Liverpool, England. "Prior to the introduction of bees from Africa," he said, "no honey was produced [for export] in that part of Brazil, which is near the equator."

It is difficult to reach any firm conclusions because there are no records concerning honey production in Brazil. Beekeeping there is not an organized business and the few statistics available do not represent the actual situation.

"Most of our beekeepers avoid giving correct information," Dr. Gonçalves said, "because they fear their taxes may increase."

There are so many people with personal vested interests in this story that I came to consider my own personal experience the most reliable gauge of the truth. I have been to Brazil, I've been attacked by killer bees, and I've interviewed the leading bee experts in both Brazil and the United States. There is no question in my mind that killer bees will reach the United States. The only question, I believe, is *when* they will arrive.

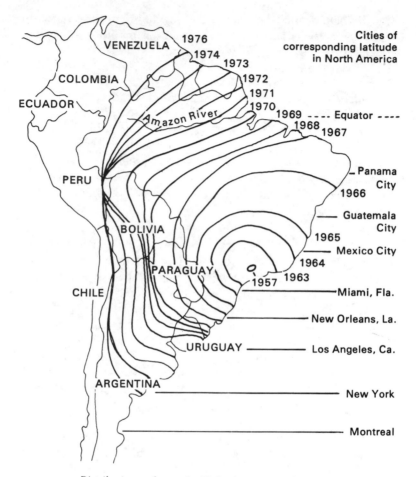

Distribution and spread of killer bees in South America.

7

The Migration

A Continent Is Alarmed

"Optimism, said Candide, is a mania for maintaining that all is well when things are going badly."

Voltaire

*"No barrier, neither mountain nor rivers, nor sea, can possibly stop **adansonii's** advance northward . . . After the first swarm of African bees, hundreds will follow, every year, forever.*

Professor N. Kempff Mercado

It is not certain exactly how fast the killer bees are moving north, but they are coming. The National Academy of Sciences team estimated their progress at 200 miles a year. Recent updates indicate they are taking the coastal route around Brazil rather than going through the interior of South America. Thus it may take them a few more years than estimated to reach the United States, but they should arrive by 1990.

But they could arrive sooner. A recent report from Georgetown, Guyana, is alarming. There is new evidence that killer bees can cross wide expanses of water. It had been assumed that the bees would have to migrate through Central America and Mexico to reach the United States. This is not true, according to Paul Allicock, a bee specialist with the Guyana Ministry of Agriculture.

Allicock believes that killer bees can cross large bodies of water, because of two recent incidents. The first report came from a Guyanese fisherman, who said he was attacked by a swarm of bees ten miles out at sea. The second was evidence of bees appearing on the once infamous French penal colony Devil's Island, in the Atlantic off French Guiana.

If this is proof that killer bees can survive at sea, it could have far-reaching implications. U.S. experts expected the bees to move northward by land, and hoped to head them off in Central America. Now, according to Allicock, it seems possible that the bees could island-hop north through Trinidad, the Lesser Antilles, the Greater Antilles, Puerto Rico, Hispaniola, Cuba, Jamaica and the Bahamas—and from there to Florida.

U.S. scientists are carefully monitoring the killer bees' northward progress. They have covered virtually all of South America. On July 10, 1974, the Venezuelan news service Ultimas Noticias reported that a swarm of Africanized bees killed 12 persons in the small town of Tapirapeco in southern Venezuela. There the bees are known as "the assassins." The story was carried in the *Washington Post.*

In Robore, Bolivia, a swarm of African bees attacked a funeral procession and sent two more persons to their graves. Ten of the mourners were taken unconscious to the hospital for treatment. Troops were called out to destroy the bees with flamethrowers.

There are reports of several other deaths in Bolivia. A Bolivian correspondent for *Los Tiempos* told me that people have been killed in Bolivia in the cities of Montero and Santa Cruz. The bees there are very nearly pure African because the bee industry in Bolivia is not well developed. Therefore the bees are extremely dangerous. Much of Bolivia is tropical jungle, an ideal condition for the killer bees. The correspondent, Avaro Christian, said that three people were killed by bees in 1972 in Sucre.

Killer bees have also penetrated deeply into Argentina. The situation there is particularly serious because commercial bee-keeping is vital to the Argentine economy. A recent news service report from Buenos Aires gives a picture of how drastic the situation is in Argentina:

The killer bees invaded Argentina from the northeast in 1968 and have extended their territorial control at the rate of 140 kilometers [87 miles] a year, killing dozens of persons and animals and threatening to destroy an important industry completely.

The dangerous African bees have already reached the environs of Sante Fe, 435 kilometers [270 miles] to the north of Buenos Aires, leaving a string of victims in their wake: human beings and large farm animals dead with more than 50 stings.

*The killer bees, scientifically known as **apis mellifera adansonii,** have retained their most destructive characteristics. These include attacks en masse upon human beings, small animals, and fowl, and pillaging of foreign beehives, causing the disapperance of apiculture in entire regions, such as the northern province of Misiones.*

The situation was defined as critical by an officer of the National Commission for Control of the African Bee, an agency of the Department of Agriculture, since Argentina ranks second among the principal world exporters of honey, following Mexico.

To maintain the production of 25,000 tons of honey per year, of which 80% is exported, an urgent solution to the problem is required for the 700,000 beehives existing in Argentina.

However, the bees' most serious threat is to agricultural production, one of Argentina's principal sources of wealth. This is because the success of pollination in farming is due primarily to the activity of bees.

The displacement of the gentle species by the savage African bees could result in the destruction of entire crops of wheat and other cereals.

There is compelling evidence of the spread of the African bee. On March 17, 1972, a report was issued by the U.S. Department of Agriculture entitled *Insects Not Known to Occur in the United States.* The report gives descriptive specifications of the killer bee and includes a map of South America showing its presence in Argentina, Brazil, Bolivia, Paraguay, Uruguay, and Venezuela.

The pamphlet also says:

Some authorities state that due to this species' aggressive behavior toward man and animals, beekeeping as we know it today in the United States could become obsolete soon after its introduction. They estimate that it could spread into the United States within 7 or 13 years.

Perhaps the most disturbing evidence of the killer bees' spread came in 1973 when the most prestigious international beekeepers' association, Apimondia, devoted an entire issue of its distinguished apicultural magazine *Apiacta* to the *adansonii* problem. What came through most clearly was the extreme concern and alarm expressed by scientists throughtout the world.

From an article by Professor N. Kempff Mecado of Bolivia:

*In 1968, **adansonii** had already reached Barra de Corda, Maranhao State, beyond which the Amazon region lies; consequently, its advance northward is 230 km annually. It spread westward to Bolivia and Paraguay 150 km a year, and southward at the same rate. The symposium on the African Bee in 1969 pointed out that by the end of 1973 the first swarms of **adansonii** would reach Buenos Aires province, and that nothing could prevent the advance of **adansonii** southward, as it had been proved that they forage at lower temperatures than the Italian bees. We must point out that the only South American country which will escape the Africanization of its bees will be Chile, as it is isolated by natural barriers."*

Professor Mercado also said that "wherever *adansonii* arrives, everything falls into confusion and most people give up beekeeping." He cited as an example the Santa Cruz district of Bolivia, where beekeeping is practiced on a small scale. Five years after the arrival of killer bees, honey production had declined by 40 percent and the price of honey had tripled.

Most of the beekeepers had given up because they were unable to work with such aggressive bees. He said the same thing happens wherever the African bee goes, and quoted an article by the president of the Paraguay Beekeepers' Association, which stated that after the African bees reached Paraguay in 1964 or 1965, "their swarms attacked the native bees in their hives, in tree hollows or in common boxes, overwhelming them. All native bees disappeared in Paraguay, being replaced by the 'Africanized' ones."

According to Mercado, "beekeeping was altogether ruined" in northern Argentina.

Commenting on the killer bees' aggressiveness, Mercado quoted an African beekeeper: "When provoked, a colony of African bees will follow the intruder even inside a dark house, which does not happen with any of the other bee races." That is exactly what happened to us after we filmed a very aggressive colony in Recife. In order to escape the bees, we went into a dark concrete storage building where, to our amazement, the bees continued to attack us.

Mercado is particularly alarmed at the numerous wild swarms of killer bees and warns:

These wild colonies can and must be destroyed by any means, but usually it is difficult to find them. The colonies must be destroyed by burning them, or by starving them by blocking hive entrances; it is not advisable to poison them, because this could also kill the gentle bees in the apiary, which would be attracted to the poisoned honey.

In 1973 the Venezuelan Minister of Agriculture, Professor M. Stejskal, said the killer bees had already invaded Argentina, Bolivia, Uruguay, and Paraguay, and he feared they would reach Venezuela and the Guianas within two years and the United States in about ten years. Professor Stejskal mentioned a cross-breeding experiment in Brazil that failed. He said the offspring of a cross between killer bees and gentle bees were "inefficient foragers and aggressive." Thus the experimenters got the worst of both sides.

Still, the Venezuelan agreed with the conclusion reached by American scientists that the "Brazilian bee cannot be exterminated; one must try to make this bee more gentle by adequate breeding and cross-breeding." He said Venezuela would try to set up "a protection belt" of gentle bees along its southern border. The United States is considering such a protective barrier against the Brazilian bee across the Panama isthmus. How this will be achieved is not yet clear.

Neither is it practical.

The most pessimistic and disturbing view came from the most famous bee geneticist in the world, Dr. Friederich Ruttner of West Germany. I had an opportunity to interview Dr. Ruttner when he was at the University of California at Berkeley in 1975. He made some rather gloomy observations about "wild swarms" and the difficulty of controlling wild hybrids, which I'll go into in Chapter 9.

The Killer Bees

Let me quote his remarks to the International Conference on the African Bee, in 1973:

> *In Brazil the European races are being quickly and completely eliminated by **adansonii**—before our very eyes.*
>
> *For beekeepers, this is a process with serious consequences; and for biologists, an unexpected experiment of immense scope. How is it possible that from only 26 absconded swarms, in only 15 years, an avalanche of **adansonii** invaded half of the huge continent of South America?*
>
> *What can be done to stop or annul this development? In my opinion, this is impossible in the tropical regions, where the colonies live and multiply themselves in the primeval forests and even in the savanna, beyond man's control. In 1971 Kerr counted 107 bee colonies per square kilometer in the Brazilian savanna.*
>
> *Only two alternatives are likely: either one will get accustomed to **adansonii**, or the whole population will be exterminated by air sprayings, and everything will be started all over again. As the latter alternative is impossible, because of the large expanse already invaded, there is nothing to do anymore but to resign oneself.*

A rather discouraging outlook.

Dr. Orly Taylor, who is keeping track of the northern progress of the killer bees, told me that the bees are moving most rapidly along the coastal savannas (rather than through the interior of South America). Taylor points out that there are very few wild populations of gentle European bees along this route. Therefore, there will be little opportunity for genetic dilution:

> *Among wild bees, selection for many of the African traits may be intensive. Thus the Africanized bees moving through northern South America might be genetically very similar to the African stocks that escaped from Kerr's apiary near Rio Claro 17 years ago.*

It is difficult to find scientists who are not worried about the spread of killer bees to the United States. *The Final Report: Committee on the African Honeybee* (June, 1972) was prepared by eight unbiased American bee experts:

Anticipated Spread of the Brazilian Bee

From southeastern Peru to Macapa in Brazil, Brazilian bees are now 1,600 to 2,000 miles from Panama. At their present rate of spread, they will take five to ten years to reach Panama. But, if they are spreading from Roraima territory (the Amazon basin), the distance is only 800 miles, and being across the Amazon, progress may now even speed up. Thus, if a defensive zone is to be established in Central America before the arrival of the Brazilian bee, methods should be well developed and ready to put into effect as soon as practicable, i.e., in four to six years. [Four years have already passed.] Advance research and planning are urgently needed.

If not hindered in Central America, Brazilian bees might be expected to reach Texas about eight or ten years after reaching Panama.

Because the southward spread of the Brazilian bee has probably been solved by failure to winter well, it seems reasonable to predict that this spread will be arrested in a few years. The Brazilian bee is, therefore, not expected to survive in the northern United States. It would, however, influence the entire continent because queens and package bees are regularly shipped from the southern states of the United States. At the present time, a high percentage of the honey bee population of the northern United States and Canada is thus replaced each year by imported bees. Therefore, the Brazilian bee would be a problem for the entire continent, even though it probably could not survive the cold winters.

The greatest danger would occur if a Brazilian queen, unrecognized as such, were to be used as a commercial breeder queen. Hundreds or thousands of her female progeny might be shipped to all parts of North America before her ancestry was recognized.

So, the killer bees are coming. The questions now are how they will get here and what their effect on the United States will be when they arrive.

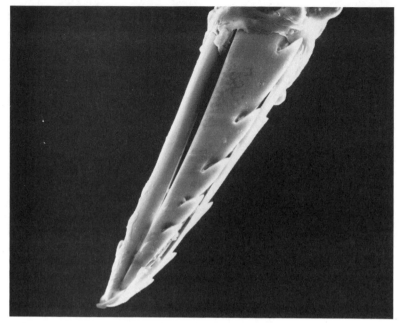

A bee stinger magnified 1500 times. The stinger is barbed and consists of two sliding shafts, which inject the venom into the victim.

8

The Threat

By Land or by Sea?

"Truth has a way of shifting under pressure."

Curtis Bok

The killer bees will arrive in the United States in one form or another. But how aggressive will they be when they reach North America? The most likely method of introduction is natural migration north — they will work their way through Central America, then up through Mexico to the United States.

The front line has already reached Venezuela by way of Surinam and French Guiana, where there are few European strains to dilute the genes. These bees are almost pure African.

Dr. Orly Taylor notes that they are moving more slowly than anticipated, probably because the dense forests and heavy rains of the Guianas create poor conditions for forage.

"I think they will build up large populations in Venezuela and then move rapidly, reaching Panama in about seven years," Dr. Taylor said. "Then it will probably be clear sailing through Mexico." Barring unusual circumstances, the killer bees should reach the United States in the early 1990s. But remember, an island route to Florida is entirely possible.

The Killer Bees

Killer bees are known to move more quickly through existing bee populations. There are a lot of bees in Mexico, since that country is the world's leading exporter of honey. The largest honey-producing apiary in the world is Miel Carlota in Cuernavaca. It produces more than 1,200 tons of honey a year, and exports 90 percent of its production to Europe and the United States. It is also an important center for rearing queen bees, which are exported to Canada, the United States, and the Latin American countries. In temperate climates it is customary to requeen hives after each winter.

Mexico is extremely vulnerable to killer bees because honey production is vital to its economy and killer bees produce more honey (25 to 100 percent more). Also, in a land noted for machismo, the challenge of handling aggressive bees will probably prove irresistible.

The owner and director of Miel Carlota, Juan Wulfrath, has 25,000 hives. "Aggressive bees always give bigger amounts of honey," he told me, "so we like our bees when they are aggressive, because we know we will have a nice harvest from them."

Wulfrath said the Mexican government is doing very little to prepare for the arrival of Africanized bees. He himself feels it is possible to work with highly aggressive bees. "We cannot avoid it," he said, "and we have to adapt our beekeeping to this new variety of bees. We have to fight this aggressiveness."

Because of the certainty of greater honey production and because of the machismo factor, there is not much concern about the killer bee in Mexico.

Wulfrath agreed that once the bees reach Central America, they will funnel through to the United States:

> There should be some work done to stop them in Central America, because that's the narrowest section and perhaps the easiest place to control the invasion. Once they hit the peninsula of Yucatan, and the country spreads and opens up to the United States, it will not be possible to stop them.

He expressed concern that "some crazy beekeeper" might take some African queens to Canada, Mexico, or the United States and start breeding them, thus nullifying any efforts made to stop the bees in Central America. But he continued to assert that beekeepers should try to work with the invaders because "aggressive bees are always good producing bees."

Perhaps the easiest way for killer bees to reach the United States is by sea. Because they swarm a lot and are migrators, it's not unusual for them to nest in the hold of a freighter.

In the five-year period, 1970-1975, there have been 43 interceptions of honeybees on ships in 14 different ports. None of them were killer bees; or it is assumed that none were killer bees. Actually, in one incident it seemed possible for quite a while that killer bees had invaded the West Coast of the United States.

On May 2, 1972, the S.S. *Argomaster* arrived in the United States with a shipment of new cars from Japan. It docked for off-loading at the West Coast depot for foreign cars at Richmond, California, across the bay from San Francisco. The freighter had stopped in Los Angeles, where it had docked next to a molasses boat from South America. When the longshoremen opened Hold No. 4, a huge swarm of bees flew out. The bees appeared very aggressive, and the longshoremen ran in all directions. Fortunately, none was stung. The cargo master quickly called the county agricultural commissioner, who sent a man down to the docks. An inspector from the Animal and Plant Health Inspection Service (a federal agency) went along.

By this time the swarm of bees had left the ship and clustered on a sling used by longshoremen to off-load cars. It was late in the afternoon, and authorities were unable to find anyone who could handle bees. The next day they found a beekeeper who destroyed the bees, which had settled on the pier. He collected about one gallon of dead bees in a plastic bag. Many bees had escaped and no queen was found among the dead bees.

Because authorities suspected that they might be Africanized bees, samples were sent to the state Department of Agriculture in Sacramento, and to Professor Howell Daly, a taxonomist (one who classifies plants and animals) at the University of California at Berkeley. Dr. Daly told me that it was entirely possible the queen had escaped:

It is not known for sure that they killed the queen. When the colony was taken apart and sent to various places, the queen was not accounted for. If she did survive, it would have been unfortunate if those bees had turned out to be African, because it is necessary to have a queen in order to establish a colony.

The Killer Bees

California entomologist Dr. Marius Wasbauer could not decide whether or not the bees were Africanized hybrids. He called Dr. Daly for a consultation. He also sent samples to Dr. Paul Hurd of the Smithsonian Institution and to world-famous bee geneticist, Dr. Friederich Ruttner, in West Germany.

Dr. Daly told me:

We were working primarily from the published literature. I'd never studied honeybees from the point of view of classifying them before. He sent me a sample of the bees, and I sat down with a microscope and, with the publications before me, tried to identify them. I realized that I was having a very difficult time coming to a conclusion because one bee would look like a genuine African bee, and another bee would look like a hybrid, while a third would look like a European bee, and yet these all presumably came from the same swarm.

Because of his difficulty in identifying the bees and the possibility that they could have been killer bees, Dr. Daly became more deeply involved. "I found it difficult, using the published information, to make a decision. And Dr. Wasbauer had the same problem, so I think there's a legitimate basis for disagreement."

Dr. Daly was searching for an objective way to identify bees:

I thought that perhaps we could use certain techniques that are now being used in classifying other organisms, where one takes many measurements on a given individual and submits these to computer analysis.

I might say the published information had never dealt with a hybrid bee before. It had only dealt with bees that one would get in Africa and bees that one would get in North America or Europe, but not a hybrid. Of course, the hybrids combine characteristics in a way that makes it difficult to separate them.

Dr. Daly said that hybrid bees combine physical as well as behavioral features, which makes it very hard to identify them. He also said that a natural or genetic accident could cause the size of the bee to vary, which would further complicate matters.

Dr. Daly's computer identification system works. It's a tedious process that involves dissecting a dead bee and measuring 25 different parts of its body—wings, legs, jaw, etc.—then entering this information into a computer. The method reduces the number of variables to a minimum, and develops a formula for each bee to be measured against.

"Hybrid bees are difficult to identify," he said, "and our technique so far seems to have offered the best promise of doing that." Dr. Daly's work is sponsored partly by the U.S. Department of Agriculture.

And what about the bees from the Richmond freighter?

As it turned out, at least according to our analyses, the bees from the ship in Richmond were not hybrid bees, and they were not African bees. They were bees from California. However, other experts have disagreed, and the situation could conceivably recur.

Dr. Friederich Ruttner happened to be visiting Dr. Daly in Berkeley at this time. Using traditional methods, even *he* had trouble identifying the bees from the freighter.

"It was too difficult for me to make a decision," Dr. Ruttner said in his thick German accent, "because I had no bees for reference. I had no samples from California, as Dr. Daly had. This is why I came here—to put our material together so that we could have references on all sides: the original European bees, the hybrids, and the bees living in the United States."

Dr. Hurd, of the Smithsonian, also was unable to make a positive identification either way, so for a while it appeared possible that killer bees had entered the United States. Though it was unlikely that a ship from Japan would harbor killer bees, its contact with the molasses ship from South America was a worrisome factor. But at least one good thing came from the Richmond freighter incident: it prompted Dr. Daly to develop a precise way of identifying killer bees.

It is not unusual for a migrating swarm of bees to nest in the hold of a ship—particularly in Brazil, where the cargo is often coffee, sugar, bananas, or other fruits, all attractive to bees.

It is very difficult for Agricultural Department inspectors to cover an entire ship when it arrives in the United States. I decided to film a routine inspection by the Animal and Plant Health Inspection Service, of a freighter that had just arrived in New York from Brazil. It was the Moore-Mac *Altair.*

The Killer Bees

The inspectors look for a lot of things—contaminated fruits or vegetables, unauthorized meat, hundreds of items. Because killer bees look like ordinary bees, identifying them on the spot is impossible, and a precise computer system in Berkeley is not going to be of much help to an inspector in New York confronted by an angry swarm of bees. The bees would be destroyed immediately, regardless of what kind they are. Then they would be identified to see if they had been a potential threat.

"I've received no instructions on the African hybridized bee," the inspector told me, "but I understand they're very similar to the European bee, so I wouldn't be able to tell the difference."

While we were filming and chatting with the captain of the ship, Turner Evans, he told us about an unusual incident he had witnessed in Brazil. It happened in 1968, in Belém, on the coast of northern Brazil, at the mouth of the Amazon River.

One morning, when we were leaving Belem, we got a message on the bridge from the lookout that the bees wouldn't let him get up to the bow. So we took the binoculars and looked up there at the bow; and we could see a swarm of bees—maybe a couple of feet long and about so wide [he stretched out his arms]—hanging off the bulwarks. There were lots of bees swarming around that swarm. So we told the lookout to get off the bow, and the mate and I put on long-sleeved shirts and hats and went up to the foc'sle head. We hit those bees from each side with fire hoses, and the swarm dropped down in the water. A few of the bees that were swarming around in the air, they kind of made as if they were going to attack us. We got them with the fire hose, and finally cleaned them all out. After it was all over, I read about the "killer bees" that had invaded Brazil, and I just figured that those were the "killer bees," because they **were** *aggressive.*

It would be a simple matter for an ambitious beekeeper, wishing to increase his honey production and therefore his profit, to smuggle an African queen into the United States. At John F. Kennedy International Airport, for example, nearly 1.7 million passengers arrive each month; at Miami International, about one million come in. Any one of them could smuggle in an African queen bee and a few worker attendants. They are shipped regularly in small wooden boxes about one inch wide and three inches long, with a sugar cube soaked in water inside and a small wire mesh opening for air.

Dr. Kerr is quite concerned about the possibility:

If an expert wants to do it, it would be very difficult to avoid. We can transport queens in a small box with candy—one queen and 20 bees can go in our pockets. But I strongly advise all American beekeepers not to try it. First, it is against the regulations of the United States Department of Agriculture. Second, it can do some harm to the American beekeeping industry.

We have received in the last two months some ten letters from American beekeepers asking us to supply them with African queens because they are impressed with their production. Of course, we have told them this is against the law and advised against trying this introduction, because it can do more harm than good to the beekeeping industry. Also it can introduce diseases that are not found in the United States now.

Dr. Marshall Levin of the U.S. Department of Agriculture told me he was glad that Dr. Kerr was not honoring requests for African queens:

That would be one of the worst things that could happen. I wish there was some way we could reach all these people. We have tried through the bee journals, and through news releases, to make beekeepers aware of the dangers of doing this sort of thing, but beekeepers as a group are very independent types and they often think they know better than anybody else. I'm just hoping that those individuals will not succeed in bringing these bees into this country.

Neither Dr. Kerr nor Dr. Levin mentioned the public, and it has occurred to me, particularly when interviewing bureaucrats in the United States, that officials are more concerned about the image of the beekeeping industry than the public welfare. It was the bee industry that triggered USDA interest in the killer bees, and the beekeepers who prompted the department to send a research team to Brazil, not concern for public welfare.

The Killer Bees

I mentioned this to Dr. Levin, since he is the man assigned to keep Africanized bees out of this country and to develop programs to deal with the killer bee.

He was starchy, condescending, and predictably evasive, mainly because he has a healthy mistrust of the media and feels that the press has exaggerated the killer bee problem. He was, however, willing to sit still for a lengthy interview, convinced that little of it would be used in the television documentary. He was right, not because we were prejudiced against him, but because his answers were lengthy, rambling, and equivocal.

The gist of his remarks was that the media had created the killer bee problem. I asked him if it was not true that people had been killed in Brazil. He answered:

> *I don't deny that there have been very severe problems in Brazil in terms of people, dogs, chickens, ducks, small animals—yes, those things have happened down there, and they could conceivably happen in this country too, **if** the Africanization took place here and **if** the resultant bees were as bad as they were down there. Now these are pretty critical **ifs**, and I don't believe at this stage of the game that we've got any business prognosticating that this will happen.*

> *This doesn't mean that we're ignoring the situation. The Department of Agriculture is concerned. We're trying to walk a very fine line between **alerting** and **alarming** people, and we don't always get very much help from certain people around the country.*

I knew exactly who those "certain people" were, but restrained my natural belligerence toward bureaucrats. I was, however, reminded of my last such encounter, the director of the National Transportation Safety Board in Washington. I was investigating a massive ammunition train explosion in California, and asked if the NTSB was taking any action. "No," said the bureaucrat, "we don't have jurisdiction because the train wasn't moving. It was sitting in the freight yards."

It has long seemed to me that the trouble with many official Washington agencies, including the Department of Agriculture, is that they often try too hard to protect the industries they are supposed to be regulating. This is inevitable because the bureaucrats are recruited from those very industries.

At any rate, in fairness to Dr. Levin, it must be said that Agriculture is doing quite a bit to combat the killer bee problem (this will be discussed in Chapter 9), and most of it is more positive than attempts to manipulate public opinion and play down the seriousness of the problem.

Still, there is whitewashing. One attempt was a syndicated television nature film called "World of Survival." It commented on killer bees but did not contain one frame of film on African bees or Brazilian hybrids. The narrator spoke of the great economic benefit these bees would have in the United States and said it would be a pity to lose such valuable creatures because of hysterical public opinion or exaggerated reporting. This narration took place while pictures of gentle European bees were being shown. The program was nothing short of a public relations film for the beekeeping industry, and contained no real reporting. It heroized the killer bee as a great friend of mankind.

Another example of manipulation of public opinion is an article that appeared in *Newsweek*, in January, 1976. Some excerpts:

> *The media buzzed with reports in the late 1960's about a lethal new breed of honeybee in South America. Swarms of these "killer bees," the stories said, worked themselves into a frenzy without the slightest provocation and attacked both people and livestock. Their estimated time of arrival was the early 1980's.*

> *But the bee's northward flight pattern has changed, and they shouldn't reach the U.S. now until about 1990. Dr. Orly Taylor, an entomologist who heads one such study for the Agriculture Department, believes that the killer bees will have cross-bred with European honeybees so often by the time they reach the U.S. that their nasty nature will have mellowed substantially.*

There is no mention that it is nearly impossible to control wild swarms or that the African genes for aggressiveness could dominate and produce more aggressive offspring. There is no mention of Dr. Frederich Ruttner's opinion that exactly the opposite could happen.

The Killer Bees

Worst of all, the article is a totally inaccurate representation of what Dr. Orly Taylor believes. It continues:

> *Another entomologist, Prof. Roger Morse of Cornell University, went to Brazil on a personal fact-finding mission and found a "well-developed, successful commercial beekeeping industry." In addition, he learned that the killer bees have inherited some of the African bee's industriousness along with its temper, with the result that Brazil now produces more honey than ever before. According to Morse, Brazilian beekeepers shrug off the danger of being stung to death by killer bees. The beekeepers say that with all the money they are making from the additional honey, they can well afford to protect themselves with an extra pair of pants.*

This is the worst kind of journalistic manipulation. In a very smug tone the article passes on the views of Dr. Roger Morse, a close friend and colleague of Dr. Kerr's, who was instrumental in helping Kerr prepare a rebuttal to the NAS report. By his own admission, Dr. Morse had dealt only with beekeepers in the São Paulo area, an area of advanced beekeeping and controlled cross-breeding. There is no mention that 90 percent of killer bees are now living in the wild. Neither is it reported that only *certain* areas of Brazil are producing more honey; beekeeping has been wiped out in other areas.

Several other articles have tried to minimize the danger of the killer bee, all of them echoing the U.S. Department of Agriculture's point of view.

It seems to me that one-sided articles are irresponsible, both those that exaggerate the problem and those that whitewash it. If I were an ambitious beekeeper reading the article just quoted, for instance, I would be very tempted to smuggle an African queen or two into the United States.

It's easy to understand why the USDA is concerned about adverse public opinion and what it views as "an antibee attitude." The stakes are high, very high: if the killer bees reach the United States as aggressive as they are now in South America, the effect could be economically devastating.

The beekeeping economy in Brazil and the rest of Latin America is based on honey production; in the United States it is based on crop pollination. The honeybee is vital to our agricultural economy, and though the adverse impact of an invasion of killer bees would not be as sensational as people and animals being killed, it would be severe in terms of dollars and cents.

Some 90 crops grown in the United States are dependent on pollination. The honeybee's value to agriculture is estimated as high as $6 billion a year. Bees play a vital role in the pollination of $1 billion worth of fruit, vegetable, and seed crops. Alfalfa, the primary feed of the livestock and dairy industries, is totally dependent on bees for pollination. Other crops affected would be onions, tangerines, mandarin oranges, cucumbers, apple, cherry and other fruit trees, and almonds. Bees are also used regularly to pollinate blueberries, cantaloupes, clover, cranberries, cut flowers, plums, prunes, and watermelons.

When bees are used to pollinate crops, the beekeeper places the hives either in the field or alongside it. Bees are in such demand for pollination that commercial beekeepers sell their services.

Killer bees cannot be used for crop pollination because they tend to migrate and swarm too much, and they are so aggressive that farm machinery most certainly would incite them to attack animals, farmworkers, and anyone else nearby.

"If our honeybees become at all like the ones in Brazil, it will be a catastrophe," a California beekeeper said. "We beekeepers could gear up to handle them, but the harvesters, irrigators, and tractor drivers—the people who have to work in the fields—would have an awful time."

Dr. Marshall Levin has said an invasion of killer bees "would almost entirely wipe out hobby beekeeping in this country. And that's a pretty major aspect of our industry, because we estimate in the neighborhood of 200,000 beekeepers and about 160,000 of those are hobbyists." The beekeeping industry does a whopping $250 million worth of business a year, selling honey, beeswax, and other bee byproducts, and most of this comes from amateurs. As Levin says, "People who play with bees are not going to want to work with wild beasts."

The Killer Bees

The National Academy of Sciences report predicted that the impact of the killer bee in North America would be severe:

*Since the worst experiences of people with bees are expected in warm climates, and since temperate Mexico and the southern United States are the areas that the Brazilian bee would first invade, there is likely to be a dramatic and immediate anti-bee reaction from the public. An unfavorable press will exaggerate the problem, as it has in Brazil. [Here again we find more concern for the image of the beekeeping industry than for the public welfare.] Beekeepers have always had difficulty in dealing with the public and consequently have fared poorly in the political arena. The problem is likely to be magnified out of all proportion, if the Brazilian bees get wide adverse press coverage. Anti-bee legislation at higher (county, state) political levels might then be expected. In addition to the **political** and **public relations** aspects of the problem, the number of serious and even fatal stingings of people would, in fact, **increase** if the Brazilian bee were to act as it does in Brazil.*

It should be remembered that 500 people died from bee stings in the United States last year—most because they were allegeric. More people are killed by bees in this country every year than by snakes, spiders, and sharks combined. The problem would intensify if killer bees entered the United States: they are more aggressive and there would be more stinging incidents.

The report went on to discuss the possible impact on pollination activities:

The greatest economic impact of Brazilian bees, should they reach North America, could be expected in connection with pollination. Many species of plants would become extinct, or at best, relatively non-productive without insect pollination.

Hives near and in cities would have to be exterminated to protect people, and hobby beekeepers would abandon their beekeeping operations. This has already happened in Brazil.

The committee also questions whether the killer bee would increase honey production. Because these bees multiply so rapidly and swarm so much, the result would be excessive competition for a fixed or limited nectar supply, and this could actually reduce overall honey production because of overstocked foraging areas.

The cost of beekeeping would increase because more time would be required for inspection, manipulation, and the harvest of honey.

Finally, entry of the killer bee into the United States would wreck the queen and package-bee industry. Queens and package bees are produced in California and the southern United States and are sold by the hundreds of thousands to beekeepers in the northern part of this country and in Canada to establish the new colonies that are needed each year in cold climates where bees cannot survive the winter.

"Canada, the primary consumer of queens and package bees, will be particularly susceptible to such a change," the report said. "Unfortunately, the primary production areas for queen and package bees in the U.S. are just the ones where the Brazilian bee is most likely to cause trouble."

Clearly, then, if the killer bees reach the United States in anything like their present form, it will be economically disastrous and certainly cause public hysteria. It is not farfetched to imagine that an enemy of the United States could cripple this country economically by smuggling in several African queens and establishing killer bee colonies.

If an invasion of killer bees occurs, we will have to make people aware of whether they are allergic to bee stings, and distribute emergency bee-sting kits to as many families as possible. In short, we would have to learn to live with the killer bee while hoping to develop ways to modify it.

The common honeybee. A genetic barrier of the docile European honeybee in Central America is the proposed solution to the northward progression of the killer bees.

9

The Solutions

A Genetic Barrier

"It is vitally important to keep Africanized bees out of the United States and Central America as long as possible."

> Marshall Levin,
> USDA

"There are no geographic or climatic barriers to prevent natural migration of the Brazilian bee to North America."

> Dr. Norman Gary,
> University of California, Davis

"It's very difficult to predict the outcome."

> Professor Friederich Ruttner,
> West Germany

Dr. Warrick Kerr, the man who unwittingly created the killer bee problem, places his faith in genetics. There is an atmosphere of urgency in his genetics laboratory at the University of São Paulo at Ribeirão Prêto. Since he has left, Dr. Lionel Gonçalves has been running the department with a sort of quiet desperation, trying to get his former mentor off the hook.

The Killer Bees

There are 400 hives at the genetics lab, each containing 10,000 bees—that's 4 million bees. The researchers are studying every possible genetic combination to breed the fierceness out of the Africanized bee. They are exposing bees to radioactive cobalt and have created mutants with open stingers that cannot inject venom. The researchers achieved this through artificial insemination and in a highly controlled laboratory environment. They have already proved that it is possible to modify this vicious bee in the laboratory.

Most members of the research team feel the killer bee problem has been exaggerated, and are confident that genetics can solve it. Perhaps they would feel less assured if they had been attacked by a nasty colony in northern Brazil.

"Genetics are absolutely predictable," Dr. Kerr told me. "We can obtain a breed that is both productive and gentle. That's possible, no difficulty with that at all."

He was standing in front of a blackboard, and, to make his point clear, he instinctively picked up a piece of chalk and outlined how it would be possible to breed the ideal bee.

"Aggressivity is quantitative," he said with confidence. "I think we can make a cross between Italians and Africans and select the strains of the qualities we want—the qualities for production, for resistance to disease, and for gentleness."

I did not question Dr. Kerr, though he seemed to be ignoring what has happened in Brazil and relying far too heavily on an unswerving belief that man can control nature. Still, he is probably the leading bee geneticist in the world, except for Dr. Friederich Ruttner.

When I interviewed Ruttner, I asked him if he agreed with Dr. Kerr, and he told me that all of Dr. Kerr's theories and principles are sound and correct, that it is possible to control bee genetics, but *only in a controlled environment.* Since most of the Africanized bees live in the wild, he doubted that they could be genetically modified with any certainty about the outcome. He also pointed out that the situation is more complex with wild hybrids that are cross-breeding with other wild hybrids:

> *You can never predict what will be the outcome of these hybrids. Of course, the more European genes you introduce to these African hybrids, the more they will be similar to the European bees and the more gentle they will be. But it depends on the selection nature makes. If you have many colonies that*

are propagating out of control, then it may be that the selection will be against the gentleness, and even if you introduce new genes, you will keep the aggressiveness of the African bees.

I told him that Dr. Kerr is hopeful that as the bees move through Central America and Mexico they will become more gentle. What did he think?

"In my opinion you can't predict this," he said. Then he gave me a basic lesson in genetics, starting with some revealing information about the nature of hybrids:

It seems to be a general event that we know from breeding work in many fields, that hybridization enhances vigor or vitality. Breeders speak about "hybrid vigor" and aggressiveness. Hybrids defend themselves better, they're more self-conscious (to speak in human terms), and we have often seen that crossing two very gentle races of bees yields aggressive hybrids.

A sobering thought. What happens, then, when two aggressive hybrids cross-breed?

Dr. Ruttner's observations are important not only because he is a universally recognized authority, but also because he is one of the few experts in the field who does not have a vested interest. Dr. Levin of the Department of Agriculture believes, along with Dr. Kerr, that the killer bees will become gentle as they move through Mexico, but Dr. Levin represents the American beekeeping industry.

Dr. Ruttner's opinion is far less optimistic:

It's general in biology that if you have two different species or races selected by nature, and if the reproduction takes place within these races or species, you can predict the outcome. But if you hybridize them both, you never can predict, because there are interactions between the two systems of genes and you never can predict these.

Now, I think it was shown by Professor Kerr that you can change the bee by introducing European genes, and all the beekeepers in Brazil showed that you can do it. But, in my opinion, it's feasible only in a region where you have control of the population.

"So," I asked him, "if you have wild swarms, is it impossible to control them?"

"If you have too many wild swarms where you can't replace the queen and introduce more European genes for gentleness, yes."

I tried to pin Dr. Ruttner down more specifically on Dr. Kerr's assumption that the bees will become more gentle as they move through Mexico. He seemed to feel that he had been tough enough on Dr. Kerr and wanted to leave him some breathing room.

I could imagine if the hybrids find in Mexico a dense population of gentle bees, and if this population at least equals this new population of hybrids, then I think it could be possible. It depends on the environment. In a tropical jungle, as in Yucatan, for instance, I would guess it would be like in Brazil—a very high population of wild bees—but I don't know about the Mexican highlands and the more dry desert areas. If you're able to maintain a high population of European bees, you could stop them.

"But," I persisted, "aren't we talking about literally millions of bees, if they move north of Panama?"

"Not millions," he assured me, "but certainly hundreds of thousands of queens or swarms. Again, it depends on the situation and how much the country is developed and how many hives of controlled bees you can maintain there."

I asked him what he thinks should be done in the United States to deal with this problem. He said we need to do more work in genetics to discover how many new changes have to be introduced into the hybrids to modify them. "Then it would be easier to predict the future development," he said.

Dr. Ruttner emphasized that, despite the difficulty in controlling wild hybrids, the ultimate solution lies in genetics. "The whole thing with the African bee in Brazil is a genetic experiment. It is one of the greatest experiments ever done."

The potential threat of killer bees to the United States simply cannot be ignored. I am trying neither to overstate nor to understate the problem, just to document the truth. It is not enough to define and describe a serious problem that may affect the public; it is also important to examine possible solutions. The course of action recommended by the National Academy of Sciences Committee *Report on the African Honeybee* will give you, the reader, an idea of the urgency of the problem:

The Committee believes that every effort should be made to prevent the Brazilian bee from reaching North America. Quarantines are recommended as essential and urgent preventative measures. Research and feasibility studies should also begin immediately. Better methods of recognizing the Brazilian bee must be devised. Research on both physical and chemical barriers must be given priority, since these methods are probably necessary to buy time for developing more permanent controls. Since information is scarce, a number of complementary strategies would appear to be the most effective approach. In any event, all approaches should be initiated promptly, since no one can await the outcome of another.

The most likely place to stop the bees is in Central America, at the narrowest part of the isthmus, the Panama Canal. Most experts favor creating a "genetic barrier," that is saturating the area with gentle Italian queens in the hope that cross-breeding will end aggressiveness. The NAS report says:

Control by genetic barriers may offer the best means for stopping northward migration of undesirable Brazilian bees. Two factors that can change gene frequency would be utilized, immigration and selection.

Immigration would be carried out by bringing in stock previously selected for the purpose, and flooding the barrier territory with desirable genes. Beekeepers would be supplied with selected stock, special apiaries would be established, and drones of barrier stock would be reared in abundance. Virgin queens in the barrier territory, therefore, would be more likely to mate with drones of barrier stock than with undesirable drones.

However, there is always the possibility that the opposite could happen: the gentle bees could become more aggressive. It should be pointed out that Africanized drones always outperform their gentler European counterparts in mating. They simply fly faster. Also, the canal zone is tropical, and Africanized bees out-compete European bees in tropical climates—this was learned in Brazil. The committee report continues:

> **Selection** *against undesirable bees in the barrier territory would be accomplished by killing wild colonies, and in apiaries by requeening both aggressive colonies and those preparing to swarm. [But we are talking about millions of bees and hundreds of thousands of queens. How could all of them possibly be killed?] Unless feasibility studies show that genetic barriers are impractical, laboratory and field work should begin promptly. Selection for non-aggressive, non-swarming, and non-migratory behavior in several lines of various origins, such as bees from northern and southern Brazil and Africa, should be initiated. As soon as strains of bees presumed suitable as barriers are available, they must be field tested in an isolated location.*

It is not hard to imagine the possibility of another genetic accident.

Dr. Kerr is very much in favor of establishing a genetic barrier:

> *I think the idea of making a genetic barrier in the Panama Canal is a very sound idea, has a scientific basis, and is feasible. If some of the bees crossed the barrier, it would be easy to get rid of them: just alert the beekeepers to check the most aggressive bees and kill the queen.*

Dr. Ruttner does not agree. He believes not only that the genetic barrier plan will not work, but also that it's possible the Africanized hybrids will mutate and adapt to North American winters. As to the Panama Canal plan, he said, "European bees do not do well in tropical zones. Dr. Kerr is wrong. You cannot guarantee the outcome. In the tropics the Africans will survive over Europeans ten to one."

He gave me this example of how African bees reproduce:

> *African bees yield 30 swarms a year. The queen lays 2,000 eggs a day at a minimum; usually it's more. In a three-month egg-*

laying period the queen would lay 180,000 eggs. In just 30 swarms this gives you 5,400,000 Africanized hybrids to deal with.

He said the bees could be modified only if the European population were bigger than the Africanized population. Beekeeping in most of Central America, particularly in Panama, is fairly crude and exists only on a small scale, as a "cottage industry" among the peasants. Even if massive cross-breeding occurred, there would be problems, according to Dr. Ruttner:

You cannot absolutely predict how hybrids would behave. There could be natural selection in hybrids for wintering and for aggressiveness. You cannot predict hybrids. Some could be more aggressive. If most bees stay in the wild, they would stay aggressive.

Since the genetic barrier solution is a long-term undertaking, the NAS committee also recommended immediate action:

"New and rigid quarantine measures should be established by all countries in North and Central America. No **apis mellifera** *at any stage, including semen, should be permitted imported to North or Central America from Africa or South America, or any other country to which African bees have been introduced. The introduction of the Brazilian bee would almost certainly be intentional, hence regulations could be stringent with little chance of injuring or inconveniencing innocent people.*

Other recommended measures include: (1) destroying swarms and absconding colonies by using trap hives (that is, luring the bees into poisoned beehives); (2) using poison baits and sprays in small localized areas (but not in large areas because of possible contamination of other insects and animals); (3) unleashing an army of bee hunters to destroy all Africanized queens; (4) creating a mechanical barrier (believe it or not, the Pentagon seriously recommended erecting a 150-foot-high net across the Panama Canal to stop the bees); (5) deliberately introducing bee diseases (this method has been ruled out because it's impossible to control).

The Killer Bees

Two of these suggestions are further explained by the committee, the destruction of swarms and the use of poison baits and sprays:

Swarms could probably be captured if large numbers of trap hives, containing attractive pheromones and bees' wax, were distributed in a strip across Central America. The trap hives could then remove the swarms from the population if toxicants were incorporated into the bees' wax inside the traps, or if one-way entrances for drones and queens entering the trap were provided.

Conventional aerial spray applications might be used to control small, localized infestations, assuming that the infestations could be detected early and delineated accurately. However, in urban areas, dense forests, and wherever native pollinators or other sensitive organisms exist, aerial sprays present severe problems. This method, therefore, could be used only in very limited emergency situations.

Poison bait stations may be useful if (1) the bait can be presented so that primarily honeybees take it, (2) the toxicants can be disguised so that they are not repellant to the foraging bee, and (3) the toxicants can be transported to the hive without seriously affecting normal foraging behavior. Some of these objectives could be achieved by micro-encapsulation of toxicants.

Micro-encapsulation is a technique of covering the poison (chemical or germ) in a gel so that it is undetectable and is protected against cold or heat. The technique was developed for the U.S. chemical-biological warfare program. It's nice to see that it may finally have a practical use.

The NAS Committee was particularly attracted to the idea of micro-encapsulation of toxicants, and recommended that besides chemical agents, "microbial agents might be distributed in the same fashion." The committee recognizes the importance of developing poison baits that kill only Brazilian bees, "while protecting man and non-target animals." Very reassuring.

The NAS report, issued in June, 1972, emphasized that research in the above areas had to begin as quickly as possible, and much of it has already begun. It is even more important, however, to learn more about the Brazilian bee as soon as possible. Several programs, funded by the Department of Agriculture, are now under way.

Although the NAS Committee recommends a multifaceted approach to controlling the killer bee, it clearly favors the "genetic barrier." To this end, the report says, it is absolutely vital to study the biology and behavior of the killer bee. This includes the following: mating behavior (flight range and behavior of Africanized drones); comparative foraging behavior studies; aggressiveness (what mechanisms excite killer bees in colony defense, and how we can protect ourselves and animals if the bees remain aggressive); swarming and migration (knowledge of the distance a colony can migrate in one year is essential for planning genetic and other barrier zones); and finally, diseases (a general survey of existing diseases in the Africanized bee).

Much of this research is already in progress under the supervision of Dr. Marshall Levin.

As the national program staff chief of the Agricultural Research Service (USDA), Dr. Levin is responsible for deciding which projects will be funded. Therefore his insights and opinions are important. He does not agree with all of the proposals in the NAS report:

> *Some of the ideas that were presented in the report, and by others since then, are a little on the far-out side. I think a number of them are technically feasible, but I think they would be economically unworkable. I'm nowhere near prepared to admit the necessity for any of these things at this stage of the game. The approach that I have been taking is: Let us do what we can to provide a natural genetic filter, instead of a genetic barrier, by encouraging and developing beekeeping at an expert level in all the countries in between. I think this is probably the most positive action we could take, and some of the countries—Panama and Costa Rica in particular—are already doing some of this on their own.*

In typically blunt language, he did admit that beekeeping in general is not very well developed in Central America. "They've got a long way to go to get those folks developed to the point where they would be helpful in supplying this biological filter, but I think time is in our favor."

The Killer Bees

Though Dr. Levin believes "the state of our art in bee genetics is pretty crude," he agrees with Dr. Kerr that natural selection during their northward migration will change the bees. "I think the experience in Brazil, where the bees have greatly changed as a result of selection pressure by beekeepers and a constant infusion of improved and selected strains, allows us to anticipate that the same evolution will take place on their northward migration."

But it must be noted that the killer bees have changed only in *southern* Brazil, and there, only in well-established apiaries, and it still has not been determined whether this change is primarily due to genetics or climate. No such change has occurred in tropical northern Brazil, which has a hot and humid climate similar to that of Central America.

Dr. Levin thinks it is important to upgrade the level of beekeeping expertise in all the countries between Brazil and the United States, so that the beekeepers will be able to recognize and handle Africanized bees, and learn how to get rid of their undesirable characteristics and replace them with desirable ones. He said he is trying to encourage these countries to increase their beekeeping and educational efforts in order to create the kind of technology that can accomplish the desired modification. The higher the population density that African genes have to work through, the greater the likelihood that they will be changed by the time they reach southern Mexico.

This aim does not take into consideration the large numbers of "wild swarms," which will be out of control. Native bee populations in Central America are dispersed, jungles are dense, the climate is tropical. For all these reasons it is hard to imagine how killer bees could be brought under control in Central America.

The Department of Agriculture has funded research projects in three areas: (1) improvement of the means of identifying Africanized hybrids (Dr. Howell Daly, University of California at Berkeley); (2) a monitoring impact study to keep track of their natural northward disperson (Dr. Orly Taylor, University of Kansas); (3) efforts to obtain a better understanding of the relationship between environment and genetics on the temper and aggressiveness of the bee (Dr. Kerr and Dr. Lionel Gonçalves, University of São Paulo).

One of the more controversial aspects of this unfolding drama is the assumption by some experts that killer bees will be unable to survive the winters in North America. The theory goes that because the bees appear to be less aggressive in the cooler temperate climate of southern Brazil, they may not be a threat to the northern United States—say, north of San Francisco in the West, and north of Charleston, South Carolina, in the East. One of the problems with this theory is that it does not take into account the hot, humid summers of most of the United States.

At present, there is no definite knowledge that the Africanized hybrid could survive a *direct* transfer to a temperate climate. However, the bee's adaptability could cause it to mutate to the degree that it could, after several generations, survive. Research is now underway to assess the ability of these hybrids to cope with a variety of different climates. This work, incidentally, is being done by Dr. Warwick Kerr's staff in Brazil.

Most American commercial-breeding beekeepers operate in the South. Northern beekeepers replenish their stock from them in the early spring. So an Africanized hybrid that looks like a domestic honeybee could enter the United States, winter in the South, and after being sent in the spring to another warm climate, develop the potential for existing in temperate climates. Remember, African bees are known for their adaptability.

In addition, Africanized hybrids lay twice the number of eggs the Europeans do and they have great breeding capabilities—three generations every summer. Large population growth is a survival characteristic. Both Dr. Daly and Dr. Norman Gary of the University of California at Davis agree that the foregoing is a possibility.

Another effort of the USDA project is to determine the role that climate and latitude, as well as genetics, play in aggressive behavior, and how the two combine to determine behavior. For example, the most aggressive bees are those around Belém, Fortaleza, and Recife in Brazil, hundreds of miles north of São Paulo. South of São Paulo, they appear less aggressive. Why is this? Dr. Levin feels it is important to find out:

> *We noticed that the bees retained their ferocity as they worked north into the tropical and semitropical part of the country, and seemed to lose their ferocity as they worked south into the more temperate climates.*

As they worked south, they were going into an area where

there was a good-sized resident population of honeybees being managed in a fairly effective and efficient manner by fairly expert beekeepers. Going north, the bees encountered no such resident population, and what few honeybees were there were not managed at what we consider a high level of expertise.

*We felt it important to try to determine just **how much** of **what** was involved under those circumstances, and this is why we asked Dr. Kerr to explore this one aspect: the relative influence of climate and environment versus the effect of genetics on these bees.*

It doesn't seem proper that Dr. Kerr, the man who created this problem in the first place, should be doing major research on the problem at U.S. taxpayers' expense. Although he is widely respected and is undoubtedly an honest scientist, he does have a unique interest in the outcome of the story. We should avoid financing scientists who might be unconsciously tempted to color the truth for one reason or another. What if Dr. Kerr discovers that the situation is worse than he thought, that the killer bees can adapt to any climate, that wild swarms are impossible to control, and that what is happening in southern Brazil is an isolated phenomenon? Would he play devil's advocate?

The work with killer bees must be done in Brazil since it is illegal (and would be foolhardy) to bring them into this country, even for research purposes. But are there not other scientists in Brazil who are qualified to do this work? It would certainly seem so. Why not finance an international committee of independent scientists to oversee all research projects on the killer bee?

Dr. Marshall Levin remains optimistic. Even if the worst happens, he feels that good old American technology will prevail:

*We would be on top of the situation as soon as it happened. We've got resources that we could muster to take care of the situation, which Brazil did not have. They didn't have the experience of a Brazil to tip them off as to what could happen, which we **do** have, so I think we're in a lot better position. We've got better technology to cope with these things, we've got better resources, we've got better educated and trained farm* *people, we've got better communications. The whole picture would be completely different.... What happened in Brazil is a biologically unique situation.*

If this book has sounded pretty grim thus far, do not despair. American ingenuity has prevailed before, and can do so again.

I'd like to share with you some letters I received after the NBC News television documentary *Killer Bees* was shown on June 7, 1975. The problem of killer bees triggered some unique startling solutions from our viewers.

To whomever:

I am writing to those who are willing to read: "The fantastic story about the African Killer Bees."

To begin with I am a student at John F. Kennedy High School in La Palma, Calif., and I presently possess an ant farm. Big deal (right?)! Well, just a few days ago I fed my ants a few bees obtained from around the school. Then I placed the bees in the cage where my ants are. Immediately the bees were attacked and eaten. If the Amazon Ant is much more aggressive than the common red ant here in southern Calif., and if the African killer bee possesses the aggression equal to the Amazon Ant, there could be a war between these two insects. If the ant's outer shell will restrain the bee sting, we might solve our problem....

Thank you,

Vickey Cuevas
Buena Park, California

Dear Sirs,

In regard to killer bees. Have you not heard that "music soothes the savage beast"? Has there been any research in using sound frequency to calm the bees or even to kill them (a frequency not harmful to humans)? Possibly transmitting the frequency to the bees' antennae?

Sincerely,

George W. Evans
Houston, Texas

The Killer Bees

Dear Sirs,

I was quite interested in your "killer bee" report on "Weekend," June 7, 1975.

Part of this report dealt with a segment in which a man working in his backyard in (Racife?) Brazil was stung in the neck by a killer bee. He slapped at the bee and was almost immediately attacked by the entire swarm, which had appeared from a drawer of an old desk which was in the yard.

Despite your report of the bees' responsiveness to vibrations, I do not believe that the sound or ground-wave vibrations caused by the man's slap can account for the bee attack. I suggest the bees have a summoning ability (possibly ultrasonic in nature) which enables one killer bee to summon its fellows.

If such a summoning mechanism exists, and can be duplicated, then by thus stimulating the aid-summons, the bees could be lured to a point where a method could be used to destroy them. Whereas such a method might not be able to destroy all the killer bees of South America, it should none-the-less be able to block the immigration of the bees at some strategic place (such as the Isthmus of Panama). If the method were successful in destroying the Africanized bees in the whole continent of South America, gentler bees (such as the common North American honeybee) could be reintroduced . . . .

Thank you,

Jon B. Slobins
Damascus, Maryland

Dear Sirs,

According to your study, as I saw it, the bees respond to a single sting by a group response in kind. This suggests to me that we might try to learn how this instant call to action is communicated—certainly not through a "bee dance" but probably a chemical messenger pheromone—and seek a technique for blocking it. Such an attack pheromone would be carried downwind, causing the kind of prolonged and distant stinging that you reported following your final bee test outside

Recife. If we must learn to live with these insects, it would be nice to have the means to countermand their attack orders.

Very truly yours,

Robert W. Zimmer, Ph.D.
Vice President, Scientech, Inc.
Boulder, Colordo

Dear Sirs,

Enjoyed your "Weekend" report covering "killer bees" very much. I feel, however, you left out two very important questions concerning the control of the hybrid bees. Two very basic questions would concern Preditor/Prey and Species Specific Diseases as means of controlling and buying time. The cat's out of the bag and they may very well be our only defense.

I believe that one major Preditor/Prey relationship exists between the wasp and the common honeybee . . . whole bee hives have been devastated.

Species Specific Diseases exist which may indeed aid in checking a rapid migration northwards. Recently a bacteria called Bacillus Sphaericus was found to be very effective as an agent for controlling mosquitoes and fly larva. Grecprines and Nematomorphs may also offer some species specific agent in the zoological area. Also, in the area of mycology exists a fungus called entomophthora muscae which is pathogenic to the common housefly.

I'm no authority on bees, but it seems to me that a concerted effort at biotic control may be effective and I sure wouldn't put any faith in deserts and canals.

Sincerely,

D. Seymour
Ypsilanti, Michigan

Gentlemen (and Mesdames),

It was with great interest that I watched the NBC program "killer bees."...I would like to address a few questions to the Doctor who imported the African (aggressive type) bees.

The Killer Bees

—*Why have they never left Africa?*

—*Is there some natural barrier that has kept these bees in Africa and on the Continent and in that Hemisphere? In this Hemisphere, they are flourishing and moving northward at a rate of 200 miles a year.*

—*What has prevented these bees from moving northward into Europe and Asia and dominating the milder bees, such as the Italian? Apparently they have dominated the local bees in South America, so why have they not moved across the land bridges into the Middle East—where there is much honey—and into Italy, where they could dominate the Italian bees?*

—*Why is this country spending thousands of dollars trying to stop the bees from moving northward from South America, when some of that money could be used to learn why they stay at home in Africa?*

Please, I'm not trying to be funny. I would appreciate a reply.

Sincerely,

Alma S. Birn
Tampa, Fla.

Dear Sir,

As a systems consultant with extensive scientific credentials, I would like to present a possible (and practical) solution which, I hope, you will forward to the proper authorities.

The solution is based upon a modification to an already accepted means of "naturally" controlling excess insect populations, i.e.,

1.   Fast breed wasps (bee wolves) by the billions in a controlled environment.

2.   Sterilize these wasps by use of X-Rays so that they will not, of themselves, present a future problem.

3.   Geographically sectionalize the "infected" areas into concentric rings of "controllable" sizes, and "seed" the wasps into each area. Naturally, the seeding procedure would be done by aircraft, and would be done to a degree sufficient to considerably reduce the native population of bees.

4. Continue this process, arc by arc, until you have completely cleared the infected areas; and thereafter (as soon as you have established at least one buffer area between the infected and non-infected areas) re-seed the uninfected areas with docile European bees.

> *Very truly yours,*
>
> *Jerome G. Ganci*
> *Brooklyn, New York*

Dear Sir:

I gather from this report that no one has been found in the scientific world who can offer a solution to this phenomenon. I therefore take the liberty to make a suggestion to you.

There is one man above all others who may be able to shed some light on this matter. He is the author of "Practical Handbook of Bee Culture, with Some Observations upon the Segregation of the Queen." I believe this book would be of great value to researchers, since the report you ran on killer bees mentioned the important role played by the Queen. The author of this book has devoted much of his time since retiring after a long and illustrious career to the study of these little (but menacing, it seems) creatures. I believe a consultation with this personage would be fortuitous before the problem gets out of hand, and I urge you to see to it that a proper representative be sent to him.

The gentleman I have mentioned lives in retirement on the Sussex Downs in England, and may be found there. He lives alone, save for a housekeeper. I feel sure he would be willing to exercise his unique talents to this threat of the killer bees. His name: Mr. Sherlock Holmes.

> *Yours faithfully,*
>
> *Bruce R. Beaman, Esq.*
> *Stevens Point, Wisconsin*

And so, American, and British, ingenuity come to the rescue.

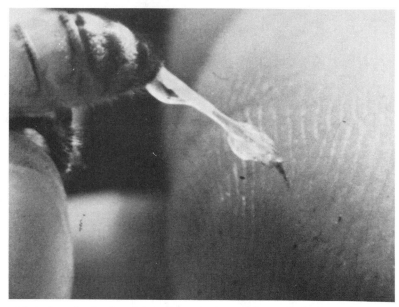

A bee stinger has just been injected into a beekeeper's finger. The bee's muscles around the venom sac thrust the barbed stinger in further. When the bee flies away, it is disemboweled and dies.

10

The Mystery

A Genetic Time Bomb

"Only error needs to be protected by government; truth will stand by itself."

Thomas Jefferson

The killer bee controversy has evolved into a rather perplexing mystery. On the one hand, from experience in Brazil, we know that the bees are vicious killers; on the other hand, we have cautious USDA bureaucrats reassuring us that, by the time the bees cross-breed their way through Mexico to the United States, they will be more gentle. There is speculation that killer bees cannot survive in temperate climates; but it is known that they are highly adaptable and could probably learn to live in cold weather—and still remain aggressive.

No one has pointed out that not only have killer bees been introduced into the United States, but their offspring are here even now.

Shortly after completing the previous chapters, I called a prominent geneticist who has been helping me verify some opinions about genetics in this book. He had come upon some recent information that is extremely sensitive and controversial. Careers are at stake and certain sources must remain anonymous in order to be protected from reprisals.

In essence, I was told that Africanized hybrid bees are now in the United States, and have created serious economic problems for beekeepers. They are not yet a threat to the public because there is not a significant wild population of them at this time, but reports of aggressive behavior are beginning to crop up.

Furthermore, the U.S. Department of Agriculture is officially covering up the entire mess.

We know that the semen of killer bee drones was introduced into the United States in 1960 and 1961. Dr. Warwick Kerr shipped the sperm of African drones from Brazil to Dr. Stephen Taber III of the USDA Bee Laboratory in Baton Rouge, Louisiana. Dr. Kerr described the bees as "very productive honey-wise and fierce." It was assumed that the shipments were limited to the sperm of only five African drones, and that only two queens survived artificial insemination. This is not true. Let me unravel the mystery.

My geneticist source told me that there were many more colonies of African hybrids in Baton Rouge than reported by the USDA, and that not all the bees were destroyed. Worse yet, the killer bee hybrids were allowed to fly freely and undoubtedly mated with bees in the Baton Rouge area—both from the National Bee Stock Center and from the commercial apiary, which reportedly sent new queens all over the United States. My source accused the Department of Agriculture of "a conspiracy of secrecy."

I was given the name of another prominent researcher, willing to risk his career to expose the truth. After a long and tiring plane trip and nearly two days of briefings, I came away convinced that the U.S. government, once again, was covering up a potentially dangerous situation. The scientist believes that the Department of Agriculture has "deliberately misled the public that the Africanized hybrids were destroyed." He has signed documentation that there was "a significant introduction of African bee genes into the Baton Rouge area in 1960-1961."

In Dr. Stephen Taber's words:

Shipments of bee semen collected by Kerr from African bees in Brazil were sent to me in 1960 and 1961. There were many shipments of three to four tubes of semen, each tube containing sperm from 20 to 40 drones.

In other words, several shipments of the semen of about 100 drones were received over a two-year period. Taber says that with this sperm he produced two colonies of bees that were 93.75 percent pure Africn *(adansonii)*. He had maintained the colonies for approximately two years when a Brazilian scientist, alarmed by incidents of killer bee attacks in the state of São Paulo, warned USDA officials that the bees were extremely dangerous. He urged them to destroy the colonies. At the time, Dr. Taber was on Christmas leave, so a superior in the department destroyed the two nearly pure African colonies.

Incidentally, one of the nearly pure African queens was sent to a geneticist with Dadant and Sons, commercial bee breeders in Hamilton, Illinois. The geneticist produced a colony from the queen, which he later said was "so nasty, vicious, and mean that we got rid of them." This was during the summer, when the weather was hot and humid.

In addition to the two potentially dangerous colonies in Baton Rouge, there were numerous others with African ancestry as high as 60 percent. These hybrid colonies were not destroyed. Dr. Taber points out that he was the only one who knew how many colonies of Africanized bees he had, and that as far as he knows, the others were eventually assimilated into the Louisiana bee population:

During that time many queens in the bee yard were of different degrees of African ancestry. The drones were not confined and could have mated with local virgin queen bees in the vicinity. Queens could have escaped, too, with swarms.

Drones were produced by some colonies and undoubtedly swarms issued and dispersed. Excluders were removed from the entrances as soon as inseminated queens began laying eggs.

Taber admits that it would have been useful to have kept notes, so he would have known how many colonies were involved, but said that because of a labor shortage, much that should have been done, wasn't. A classic understatement.

He continues:

The only colonies and stocks destroyed (by O. Mackenson while I was on Christmas vacation) were the F4 generation [that is, the two colonies of 93.75 percent pure Africans]. In addition ten to twenty colonies of various African hybridization were maintained for three or four years at the Baton Rouge Bee Lab. These colonies were not destroyed.

The Killer Bees

In view of what happened in Brazil in 1957, what happened in Baton Rouge, Louisiana, in 1960-1961 seems incredibly reckless. It is probable that at the time Dr. Taber was not yet aware of the possible consequences; in fact, he wrote Kerr in 1965, asking him to explain the *Time Magazine* article about "Brazil's Killer Bees." But Dr. Kerr, it would seem, should have known that the semen experiments were risky.

Also, the Department of Agriculture must go on record as having known about the imported African bee semen, because the shipments are logged in its official *Quarterly Reports* for the Baton Rouge Bee Laboratory.

Now, fifteen years later, Agriculture prefers to conceal the fact that it allowed the offspring of killer bees to cross-breed with bees in the United States—and without adequate quarantine measures.

A highly respected entomologist at the University of Georgia, Dr. Murray Blum, worked with Dr. Taber on some of the breeding work at Baton Rouge. He has verified the fact that the Africanized drones were allowed free flight; that some of the Africanized colonies were seen swarming; and that they undoubtedly mated with bees in the Baton Rouge area.

Yet, the Department of Agriculture spokesman, Dr. Marshall Levin, testified at a Senate hearing considering legislation to prohibit the importation of African honeybee semen, that "we destroyed all known sources of that germ plasm in the country."

Dr. Taber and Dr. Blum have said that Levin has never talked to either of them about what happened at Baton Rouge. Since they were the only two people with any knowledge about the matter, there is no way Levin could have known the facts.

In addition, Dr. William Wilson, reasearch leader at the Department of Agriculture's Bee Research Laboratory in Laramie, Wyoming, has told my sources the "long before Levin testified before the Senate Committee, I showed him material indicating that a large amount of *adansonii* semen had been imported into Baton Rouge and that all of the Africanized colonies had not been destroyed."

It appears either that Dr. Levin's only source of information was hearsay, and he assumed that all the colonies were destroyed; or that he was covering up an embarrassing situation. Why didn't he ever talk to Dr. Taber or Dr. Blum? Why didn't the National Academy of

Sciences team go to Baton Rouge to find out what happened to the African bee stock that was introduced into the United States?

Compounding the problem is the fact that Dr. Taber sent African bee semen to a geneticist at the University of California at Davis in the Sacramento Valley. The offspring reportedly were allowed to fly freely and mate with the existing bee population.

Now, the crucial question: If African bee offspring are in the United States, what happened to them?

The unraveling mystery:

Shortly after the Kerr/Taber semen experiments in 1962, beekeepers in Louisiana and California began to notice that a mysterious malady was affecting thousands of colonies of apparently healthy bees. The bees simply disappeared from their hives and died; the colonies were so weakened that they also died. Scientists have not been able to determine the cause; it was not starvation, pesticides, or any known bee diseases. For lack of a better name, the malady has been called "disappearing disease."

Dr. William Wilson has compiled extraordinarily convincing documentation that links "disappearing disease" to the introduction of African bee stock into this country.

An outline of the situation is contained in Clarence Bensen's angry letter to Congressman Thomas Foley, chairman of the House Committee on Agriculture. Bensen is president of the American Honey Producers Association.

> *During the past several years a malady has affected the colonies of a number of beekeepers. Bees simply disappear from the hives until the colonies become non-existent . . . The American Honey Producers Association has, for the past several years, passed a resolution at its annual convention requesting that research be conducted to determine the cause of this "disease." Levin has consistently refused to have any research done on the problem.*

> *Dr. William Wilson, being concerned with bee diseases, has compiled considerable information on losses due to "disappearing disease." He has developed a hypothesis attributing the "disappearing disease" to the introduction of African bee stock into the state of Louisiana (where the disease*

is prevalent), and in his opinion, in other areas of the country. This hypothesis is partially based on the supposition—or fact—that Africanized bees do very poorly in temperate climates. Levin has ridiculed Wilson's hypothesis. It is natural that he would do so because to give any credence to the hypothesis would be contrary to his contention that there has been no infiltration of Africanized stock into colonies in the United States.

Dr. Wilson believes that the "disappearing" bees are African hybrids, and that they are dying out because African bees cannot survive cold weather. The mysterious deaths usually occur in late fall or early winter—almost always when the weather is near freezing, or when it is cold and raining.

Beekeepers first began to notice this phenomenon in 1961. Two significant articles appeared in bee journals in 1965 and 1966, when scientists in Baton Rouge and Sacramento became alarmed. Dr. E. Oertel of the USDA Bee Lab in Baton Rouge wrote:

Thousands of colonies died in south-central Louisiana and northeast Texas. . . . A Louisiana man with 55 years of beekeeping experience stated that he had never before seen anything like it.... Probably between 4,000 and 5,000 colonies either died or became extremely weak in a relatively small area in Louisiana.

The USDA scientist and his staff investigated the unusual deaths, but were unable to determine the cause. Dr. Oertel said that "apparently the worker bees died in the field because only a few dead bees could be found" in the hives. After extensive testing at the USDA Research Labs in Beltsville, Maryland, all known bee diseases were ruled out as the cause. Dr. Oertel concluded:

As it now stands, we only know that in the fall of 1963 and the winter of 1963-64 there was an unexplained severe loss of honeybee colonies in a few relatively small areas.

In 1966 an article by H. Len Foote of the California Department of Agriculture noted that:

During recent winters beekeepers in some parts of California have been puzzled by what appears to be a rather rapid disappearance of bees from their hives. Strong colonies, heavy with honey and pollen, apparently at their prime for overwintering, suddenly start to decline for no apparent reason during autumn, and collapse within six weeks.... The disorder has caused loss of up to 90% of the colonies in affected apiaries....

The disorder was first noticed during the winter of 1961-62, when affected colonies were found at a number of locations in the Sacramento Valley, including research colonies at UC Davis. Similar losses occurred in USDA research colonies at LSU, Baton Rouge, Louisiana.

He said the bees leave the hive while still able to fly and die unnoticed some distance from the apiary.

The mystery became more intriguing when I read several letters from beekeepers to Dr. Wilson. Some excerpts follow:

My bees have not been normal for nine years [this was in 1973]. Our first trouble traces to queens received from a large southeastern breeder.

We are now operating 2,000 hives short of our usual number. ...This year has almost been a disaster. We started losing bees and hives from spring a year ago and it has not stopped....Bees are almost always mean and nervous. When a hive is opened, fifty to a hundred bees zip out to attack."

This Nebraska beekeeper said that many of his hives had become affected by bee diseases not common in this country, and that many other beekeepers nearby were having the same problems.

In another letter, dated February 2, 1976, a beekeeper told of excessive swarming of his bees during the winter, and that the bees of one colony flew out of their hive to forage. The temperature was 7 F. and the sun was shining. The bees died.

In another letter, a beekeeper said:

I observed a colony flying at the rate of one bee every minute or so. The unusual thing about this occurrence was the temperature: -14 F. The sun was shining in the winter entrance and the bees within were uncommonly active.

The Killer Bees

Finally, a letter dated November 20, 1975, from a beekeeper in Florida raises the question that had not occurred to the others:

Several commercial beekeepers have had their hives turn vicious, and there is concern that maybe the African bees are already in Florida.

Dr. Wilson's theory was becoming more and more difficult to refute. He explained to me that the attributes that have enabled the African bee to survive the harsh environment of Africa are causing it to die in temperate climates. Since cold temperatures were not encountered in their evolution, they do not respond to temperature, but to light only. European bees, on the other hand, react to both light and temperature. Because African bees have more sensitive eyes (or light meters), they work early in the morning and continue until later afternoon. In other words, if there is light, they will leave the hive to forage for food no matter how cold it is.

A researcher working with pure African bees in Poland reported that they try to forage whenever the sun is shining, even if it's freezing. In cold weather their muscles slow down, they become immobilized, and they soon die.

According to Dr. Wilson, this is apparently what causes the mysterious malady called "disappearing disease."

This does not mean that killer bees cannot live in the United States. African bees have never been challenged to survive in cold climates. Remember, they are highly adaptable. A leading geneticist has told me that future generations of these bees could easily adapt to cold weather. He explained that nonsurvival (or death) is the key to eliminating genes that cannot compete. If there are 100 colonies of bees and 90 die out, the surviving 10 colonies could, in succeeding generations, produce offspring that would be able to adapt to cold weather. In effect, they get rid of weak genes so their progeny will survive.

The Africanized hybrids in the United States live in commercial apiaries; a significant wild population has not developed yet. When it does, the bees most likely will be forced to adapt to our temperate climate. They most certainly will be able to flourish in warm southern states like Florida or the Southwest. Most parts of the United States are hot and humid during the summer—and killer bees thrive in hot, humid climates. Also, it took Dr. Kerr's original African swarms five to ten years to build up a strong wild population. It could happen here.

In populations genes can accumulate for no particular reason, strictly by chance. At any time the combination of genes could come together through natural selection, which would enable the Africanized hybrids to survive in temperate climates.

If Dr. Wilson's theory is true, the most immediate impact of "disappearing disease" is economic. It is wiping out thousands of colonies of bees used for honey production, pollination, and queen breeding.

The most disturbing aspect of this unfolding mystery is the fact that aggressive behavior can appear in these bees at any time. Just because a bee is only 10 percent African does not mean that there's a 90 percent chance it will not be aggressive. It means that 10 bees out of 100 have dominant African traits, and the ability to pass on their aggressiveness. Every bee expert I've talked to agrees it is possible for these African hybrids to become vicious—all it would take is the right genetic combination and the right environment. If conditions in the United States had been the same as they were in Brazil, we could have had a disaster similar to Dr. Warwick Kerr's.

The Department of Agriculture has let down the American public on two counts: by carelessly introducing African honeybee stock into the United States, and by covering up the fact that the offspring were not all destroyed. It should launch an investigation immediately to determine what impact the Africanized hybrids have had in the United States, and what can be done about them. If wild populations are allowed to build up in warm southern climates, then we can expect the worst.

Admitting there is a problem is the first step toward solving it. It is imperative to end the official secrecy—particularly since the tide could turn, unpredictably, at any time.

We are, in fact, living with a genetic time bomb.

The author with some of the NBC News camera team, looking like spacemen to film aggressive killer bees in Recife. It was necessary to buy special, heavy protective clothing and line the veils with gaffer's tape. Nevertheless, Aaron Fears, cameraman, was still stung several times.

Epilogue

"The struggle between man and insects began long before the dawn of civilization, has continued without cessation to the present time, and will continue, no doubt, as long as the human race endures. We commonly think of ourselves as the lords and conquerors of nature. But insects had thoroughly mastered the world and taken full possession of it before man began the attempt. Since the world began, we have never yet exterminated—we probably shall never exterminate—so much as a single insect species."

Dr. Stephen A. Forbes,
entomologist,
University of Illinois, 1916

It has been 60 years since Forbes uttered his ominous warning, and today it rings truer than ever. Will insects inherit the earth? Can man control nature, or is Dr. Kerr's folly now an unbridled genetic experiment, and totally out of control? What will the future bring? Three recent news developments reveal more than anything else what to expect.

On December 6, 1975, the Brazilian daily newspaper *Jornal do Brasil* contained a chilling headline: "African Bees Attack 1,500 People in the South."

The dateline was Pôrto Alegre, the largest city in southern Brazil, about 500 miles from the Argentine border. Here is what happened.

Epilogue

At about 10 A.M. on December 5, fruit trucks from Passo de los Libres in Argentina gathered at the international bridge connecting Argentina and Brazil over the Uruguay River. The Argentine farmers were taking their fresh produce to market in the Brazilian city of Uruguaiana, across the international bridge. The truck farmers were waiting for the Argentine Customs House to clear them. Hundreds of tourists were also waiting on the bridge.

Suddenly there was a loud buzzing sound and the frightening, high-pitched **zzziiiii** filled the air as a massive swarm of killer bees descended on the bridge, attracted by the smell of fresh fruit.

There were 1,500 people on the bridge when the bees attacked. In panic and confusion they ran in every direction—some darted into nearby fields, others hysterically jumped off the bridge into the Uruguay River, still others went into shock or fainted. The bridge looked as though it had been strafed by an attacking aircraft: bodies lay strewn about, injured victims screamed and cried, tourists lay on the road, covering themselves with clothing and huddling next to the bridge's railing, cars were abandoned or stalled. The mass hysteria only made the bees more angry in the frantic lust for nectar; they covered the fruit trucks in a huge mass, and enraged by the confusion, stung everyone in sight.

Of the 1,500 people on the bridge, 1,019 were stung so badly they had to be taken to the hospital in Passo de los Libres. Twenty of the victims remained hospitalized in serious or critical condition. Many tourists escaped serious injury by locking themselves in their cars (the attacking bees then continually bounced off their windows).

Argentine soldiers ran into the Customs House on the bridge and locked themselves inside. The mayors of Passo de los Libres and Uruguaiana dispatched seven ambulances and all the private cars and other vehicles they could find to help the victims and take them to hospitals.

The attack was so intense and relentless that the fire departments of both cities fought the bees for several hours before they could disperse them.

In Uruguaiana 140 victims were treated in that city's hospital emergency room. One of the victims had been stung 60 times in the face and head and was in serious condition. Because the emergency room was overcrowded, a Catholic infirmary cared for 22 other victims, many seriously stung. Across the border in Argentina, eight victims remained hospitalized.

This incident occurred at the extreme southern tip of Brazil, at the Argentine border where Africanized bees aren't supposed to be aggressive.

What happened? Why was the attack so vicious? Even in summer killer bees were considered to be more gentle in the temperate south.

Two other news items shed an ominous light on the killer bee problem.

The second reported the increasing resistance of insects to pesticides. A National Academy of Sciences study released in early 1976 stated that "more than 200 anthropod species have developed immunity to pesticides during the past 50 years." The report recommended other methods of pest control, including the use of natural predators and *genetic manipulation.*

This brings us to the third news item, of January 23, 1976: the National Institutes of Health, alarmed at the possibility of genetic accidents, issued guidelines to control all genetic experiments.

The specific area of concern is the field of genetic manipulation, called "recombinant DNA research" or the art of gene transplants. There is concern that man's technology is outreaching his ability to control it.

Scientists have learned to synthesize an animal gene. They know how to transplant the genetic material of one cell into cells of an entirely different species. We are at the dawn of an age when man can tamper with the reproductive processes of nature to a degree never previously imagined, designing bacteria, plants, and other living creatures according to his own specifications.

If it sounds ominous, it is.

This brings us back to Dr. Kerr and the killer bees.

Insects first appeared on the earth 400 million years ago. They are well equipped to survive most challenges; indeed, adaptation is the insect's greatest survival characteristic.

There are as many as five million insect species, and we have identified and named less than a million. Each subspecies has adapted to specific environmental situations. This brings us back to the Argentine-Brazilian incident.

The killer bee is a formidable antagonist. Along with the insects' remarkable adaptability, it has the added advantage of being a member of a society that is totally efficient and incredibly adapted to the propagation of the species.

Epilogue

The honeybee society behaves as a single organism; individuals are assigned specific roles for the benefit of the whole. Their behavior is dominated by *altruism*—that is, each individual will instinctively give up its life for the good of the group.

Workers supply the hive with food and defend it; drones exist only to reproduce and die (so as not to waste the precious food supply); and there is the queen, the egg layer and prime mover, the focal point of the social organism. It is a perfect society, a utopia governed by one strict rule: the greatest good for the greatest number.

Dr. Kerr's genetic experiment is precisely the kind that is dangerous. Because controls were inadequate, the entire South American continent has been invaded by killer bees. There were also no controls in experiments with killer bee semen in Baton Rouge, and we do not know yet what the outcome will be.

When man tampers with nature, one can never be sure of the outcome. What if the worst occurs? The ability to develop immunity to insecticides is precisely the kind of survival characteristic that could produce killer bee hybrids adaptable to any climate, bees that could, as efforts are made to modify or destroy them, become more aggressive.

The prospect gives credibility to the chilling prophecy of *The Hellstrom Chronicle*:

"If any living species is to inherit the earth, it will not be man."

Man may have reason, but the insect has adaptability.

Appendix

Glossary*

In order to grasp the scope and severity of the killer bee problem, it is important to understand certain technical terms used in beekeeping. Briefly, here are some of the more common terms.

Alarm-Defense System. Defensive behavior that also functions as an alarm signaling device within the colony. Examples include the use by certain ant species of chemical defense secretions that double as alarm pheromones.

Alarm Pheromones. A chemical substance exchanged among members of the same species that induces a state of alertness or alarm in the face of a common threat.

Altruism. Self-destructive behavior performed for the benefit of others.

Apiary. A place where honeybees are kept; specifically, a group of hives.

Bee Stings. The worker bee stinger is barbed, and in the act of stinging, it is torn from the bee. It has a venom-filled poison sac and muscles attached that continue to work the stinger deeper into the flesh for several minutes, increasing the amount of venom injected. The stinger should be immediately scraped loose—but not grabbed or squeezed as these actions will inject more venom. Normal reaction to a bee sting is immediate intense pain at the site of the sting. This lasts for a minute or two and is followed by a swelling and reddening at the sting site, which may spread an inch or more. Swelling may not become apparent until the following day.

Occasionally, acute allergic reactions develop from a sting. In a severe allergic reaction symptoms are extreme difficulty in breathing,

*From *The Insect Societies*, Edward O. Wilson (Cambridge, Mass., The Belknap Press of Harvard University Press, 1971).

147

irregular heartbeat, splotched skin, swelling, redness, speech difficulty, prostration, vomiting, trembling, and coma. If not medically treated immediately, death will result.

Brood Cell. A special chamber inside the hive built to house eggs and larva.

Colony. A group of individuals other than a single mated pair that constructs nests or rears offspring in a cooperative manner.

Drones. Drones are reared only when the colony is populous and there are plentiful sources of nectar and pollen. They usually live a few weeks, but are driven from the hive to perish during cold weather, short food supply, or an extended period of adversity. *The only duty of the drone is to mate with the queen.*

Honeybees. Honeybees belong to the order of Hymenoptera, which is the third largest and most beneficial to man among the insect orders. Collectively, the Hymenoptera are most important to man as pollinators of wild and cultivated flowering plants, parasites of destructive insects, and makers of honey. Honeybees are social insects, noted for providing their nests with large amounts of honey. A colony of honeybees is a highly complex cluster of individuals that functions virtually as a single organism. It usually consists of the queen bee, a fertilized female capable of laying thousands of eggs a day; from a few to 60,000 sexually undeveloped females (the worker bees); and from none to 1,000 male bees (drones). The female of most species of bees is equipped with a venomous sting.

Honeybees are not domesticated; those living in a man-made domocile called a beehive or hive are no different from those living in a colony in a tree.

Mass Communication. The transfer of information among groups; information of a kind that cannot be transmitted from a single individual to another.

Melittology. The scientific study of bees.

Monogyny. The existence of only one functional queen in the nest (as opposed to polygyny).

Patrolling. The act of investigating the nest interior. Worker honeybees are especially active in patrolling and are thereby quick to respond as a group to contingencies when they arise in the nest.

Pheromone. A chemical substance, usually a glandular secretion, that is used in communication within a species. One individual releases the material as a signal and another responds after tasting or smelling it.

Piping. The sound emitted by young honeybee queens after their emergence. It induces return calls ("quacking") from other virgin queens still in the royal cells and stimulates swarming behavior by the workers.

Propolis. A collective term for the resins and waxes collected by bees and brought to their nests for use in construction and in sealing fissures in the nest wall.

Queen Bee. The first queen to emerge, after the mother queen departs with the swarm, immediately attempts to destroy the others. If two or more emerge at the same time, they fight to the death. When the surviving virgin is about a week old, she soars off on her mating flight; frequently she mates with more than one drone while in the air. She may repeat the mating flights for two or three successive days, after which she begins egg laying. She rarely leaves the hive again, except with a swarm.

Sufficient sperm are stored in her sperm pouch to fertilize all the eggs she will lay for the rest of her life. The drones die in the act of mating.

The queen usually lives for about a year, although occasionally one will live for several years.

Queen Control. The inhibitory influence of the queen on the reproductive activities of the workers and other queens.

Swarming. When the colony becomes crowded with adult bees and there are insufficient cells in which the queen can lay large numbers of eggs, the worker bees select a dozen or so tiny larvae that would otherwise develop into worker bees. These larvae are fed copiously with royal jelly, a whitish food with the consistency of mayonnaise that is produced by certain brood-food glands in the heads of the worker bees. The cell in which the larva is developing is stretched downward and enlarged to permit development of a queen. Queens, incidentally, are larger than workers. Shortly before these virgin queens emerge as adults from their queen cells, the mother queen departs from the beehive with the swarm. Swarming usually occurs during the middle of a warm day, when the queen and a portion of the worker bees (usually from 5,000 to 25,000) suddenly swirl out of the hive and into the air. After a few minutes' flight, the queen lands, usually on a tree branch, but often on a roof, a parked automobile, or even a fire hydrant. All the bees settle into a tight cluster around her while a handful of scouts search for a new home site.

When the scouts return to report on their success, there begins one of the most fantastic methods of communication in the insect world—a series of dancelike movements called the "waggle dance." Information about food sources and a new dwelling place is given by the dance and received through the antennae of the waiting bees. The location and relative richness of the food source is indicated by a round dance. A tail-wagging dance means the food is more than 260 feet away. The number of dance cycles performed by the bee is in inverse ratio to the distance of the food source. The tail-wagging dance announces the distance of a new hive site or nesting place, and, if suitable, the swarm moves en masse.

Swarming is the natural method of propagation.

Waggle Dance. The dance whereby workers of various species of honeybees communicate the location of food finds and new nest sites. The dance is basically a run-through of a figure-eight pattern, with the middle, transverse line of the eight containing the information about the direction and distance of the target.

A further note on the waggle dance, as applied to the Africanized bee: The African bees in Brazil are said to be more efficient foragers, to work longer hours, and to carry larger nectar loads per body weight. It is also believed that killer bees have an ability to communicate more accurately with their companions during the figure-eight waggle dance that indicates distance, quantity, and direction of flowers (food supply). The African bees, natives of the southern hemisphere, adapted without problems to the sun's position over Brazil. European bees apparently still operate under a genetic handicap, even though they were first brought to Brazil more than 200 years ago. The European bees seem unable to pass on exact information because they are still unaccustomed to the position of the sun in the southern hemisphere, and thus search more at random to locate flowers. The information conveyed in the waggle dance is dependent on the position of the sun, which determines the direction of the figure-eight's transverse line.

Worker Bees.   Worker bees live about six weeks during the active season, but may live for several months if they emerge as adults in the fall and spend the winter in the cluster. As the name implies, worker bees do all the work of the hive, except egg laying. It is the worker, equipped with a venomous sting, that protects the hive. *Workers die after the act of stinging.*

Recommended Precautions

If the killer bees do reach the United States, because of their viciousness there undoubtedly will be mass stinging incidents. The possibility of being allergic to bee stings should not be taken lightly. Everyone should check this with his or her doctor. The fact that a person was stung once or twice and did not suffer an allergic reaction does not mean that the next time there will be no problem.

If the killer bees do invade this country, it will be essential to know how to minimize the possibility of being stung, and what to do if one is stung. One of the country's leading allergists, Dr. Claude A. Frazier of Asheville, North Carolina, has given me permission to quote excerpts from his recent article in the *Journal of American Medicine* (May 31, 1976) entitled "Insect Stings—a Medical Emergency."

A generalized systemic reaction to a single insect sting can present a medical emergency that can result in death within 10 to 15 minutes. Since it is estimated that eight in a thousand individuals are allergic to insects and that four of these eight are severely sensitive, the potential for trouble is great. In fact, there are more fatalities annually due to insect stings than to snakebites.

Symptoms of a generalized systemic reaction can range from the mild to the severe. Such reactions can be delayed, presenting serum sickness-like symptoms of fever, headaches, malaise, urticaria (hives), lymphadenopathy (swollen lymph glands), and polyarthritis (inflamed joints). It is an immediate reaction, however, that presents the physician with a medical emergency.

A moderate systemic reaction may be marked by any of the symptoms mentioned and two or more of the following: (1) constriction of throat or chest, (2) abdominal pain, nausea, vomiting, (3) dizziness, (4) wheezing, and (5) generalized edema.

A severe systemic reaction may include any of these symptoms and two or more of the following: (1) labored breathing, (2) difficulty in swallowing, hoarseness or thickened speech, (3) weakness, (4) confusion, and (5) a feeling of impending disaster.

A shock or anaphylactic reaction would exhibit any of these symptoms in addition to two or more of the following: (1) lowered blood pressure, (2) cyanosis (turning blue), (3) collapse, and (4) incontinence and unconsciousness.

These systemic reactions are medical emergencies. The most important step in treatment is the immediate subcutaneous injection of 0.2 to 0.5 ml of epinephrine (adrenaline) for an adult and no more than 0.3 ml of epinephrine for a child. If it is possible to apply a tourniquet above the sting site, this may help lessen the rate of venom absorption. Intramuscular antihistamines are indicated: diphenhydramine hydrochloride, 0.5 to 1.0 ml of a 50-mg/ml solution, or chlorpheniramine maleate (100 mg/ml). Since epinephrine is short-acting, the patient must be watched closely for signs of returning shock, and small doses of epinephrine should be injected repeatedly as often as every 15 or 20 minutes as needed.

Oxygen should be administered to the cyanotic patient (turning blue because of inadequate oxygen in the blood), while measures to support blood pressure and circulation are mandatory.

Unless further treatment for damaged tissues or related problems is indicated, the patient usually recovers quickly and can even be discharged within a few hours.

The physician's responsibility, however, does not end with the successful treatment of the acute episode. The patient is

*totally vulnerable and may die quickly if stung again.
Desensitization should be begun at once . . . .*

*During the desensitization procedure, the patient is still very
vulnerable . . . . Therefore, I prescribe an insect sting kit and
instruct my patient to keep it handy whenever and wherever he
is likely to encounter Hymenoptera. Such a kit can be a
lifesaver and can provide for time to get the victim to medical
assistance.*

*The kit contains a preloaded syringe of epinephrine to be
injected under the skin, a tourniquet to be applied above the
sting site when possible, several antihistamine tablets, and
usually several 16-mg tablets of phenobarbital. Instructions
accompanying the kit are so complete and simple that almost
any layman could follow them when confronted by an
emergency situation.*

Doctor Frazier believes that emergency insect-sting kits should be
a standard first-aid supply wherever the public might encounter
Hymenoptera (bees, wasps, hornets).

He also recommends that his allergic patients wear a medical
warning tag or bracelet and carry a card in their wallet designating
their allergy. Many unconscious insect-sting victims die because their
allergic reaction has been misdiagnosed as a heart attack.

Dr. Frazier also warns his patients to avoid, as much as is humanly
possible, being stung in the first place:

*1.   Have nests around the home and yard periodically
destroyed while still manageable.*

*2.   Do not go barefoot or wear sandals outdoors from April to
October.*

*3.   Do not wear bright, flowery clothing. Bright colors attract
bees.*

*4.   Wear long pants, long-sleeved shirts, and gloves when
working among flowers or fruits.*

*5.   Avoid wearing anything bright that shines, such as jewelry
or buckles.*

6.   *Do not use scented lotions, soaps, shampoos, or perfumes.*

7.   *Wear light colors, such as white, light green, tan, and khaki.*

8.   *If bees are encountered,* **do not swat. Retreat slowly. If retreat is impossible, lie face down and cover head with arms.**

How will a person know if he's allergic to insect stings? A Harvard University allergist, Dr. Harry Mueller, says, "If you're bitten or stung and something happens to a part of your body other than the site of the bite, that's when to call the doctor—if you're bitten on the hand and your face swells, or you get hives all over, or go into shock."

People with very severe localized reactions—such as extreme swelling at the site—are also advised to seek medical help. "You may only get one warning," Dr. Frazier remarked. "The next time you may be dead."

Instructions for Bee-Sting Kit

1. If bites are on an extremity, apply tourniquet between the bite and the trunk of the body. Release for 3 minutes every 15 minutes.

2. Give one tablet of antihistamine by mouth immediately. Repeat in 3-4 hrs. if necessary.

3. Break vial of epinephine (adrenaline) and draw contents (1.0cc) into syringe. Swab area of skin on arm or leg with alcohol swab, inject 1/3 to 1/2cc immediately. Save syringe, and remaining adrenaline, and cover needle with needle-cover so that a second injection may be given if needed.

There are two types of dangerous reactions to insect bites in people who are particularly sensitive:

1. Anaphylactic shock—immediate collapse. Follow instructions for administration as above, but give 1cc of adrenaline immediately. Repeat in 20-30 minutes if no response.

2. Allergic asthma—sudden shortness of breath with noisy (wheezing) respirations. Follow instructions above—giving 1/3-1/2cc of adrenaline.

Less serious reactions resemble hives. These will respond to antihistamine alone, but a small dose of adrenaline may produce more rapid relief.

Index

pheromones, 64, 128-29, 147, 149
Phospholipase A, 69-71
poison, 121-22
Poland, 61, 140
propolis, 149

quarantine measures, 121
queen bees, 102, 146, 149; killing, 65;
   shipment of, 134, 135, 136
queen control, 149

Recife (Brazil), 38, 39, 40-45, 52, 64, 65,
   83-88, 91, 97, 125
recombinant DNA research, 145
Rio de Janeiro, 23, 31-32, 36-37, 52, 55
robbing, 66
Root, A. I., 40, 41
Ruttner, Friederich, 97-98, 104, 105, 109,
   116-18, 120-21

São Paulo (Brazil), 29-31, 32-33, 35,
   36-38, 49, 51, 55, 110, 125, 135
São Paulo, University of, 47, 52
semen, 54, 55, 56, 134, 136, 146
Seymour, D., Jr., 129
Shipman, William, 67-68
Slobins, Jon B., 128
Smithsonian Institution, 104
Sommer, Paulo, 62-63, 90
sound frequency, 127
South America, 22, 66, 90, 93, 98, 99
South Carolina, 125
Stejskal, M., 97
stinger, 41, 43
stings. *See* bee stings
Surinam, 52, 90, 101
swarms and swarming, 63, 66, 118, 120,
   123, 139, 149-50

Taber, Stephen III, 54, 55-56, 134-36,
   137

Tanzania, 49, 83
Taylor, Orly, 90-91, 98, 101, 109, 110,
   124
Texas, 99, 138
Time, 38, 55, 56, 136

United States, 48, 97, 101, 118; beekeeping industry, 87, 95, 111, 124,
   137-40; killer bees in, 38, 52, 53, 54, 57,
   63, 67, 93, 98-99, 101, 103-105, 107-13,
   133-41
U.S. Army, 67-71
U.S. Department of Agriculture, 22, 53,
   55, 57, 67, 95, 105, 107, 108-109, 110,
   117, 124, 133, 134; Agricultural
   Research Service, 123; cover-ups,
   133-37, 141; research labs, 134, 136,
   138
U.S. Senate, 136
Uruguay, 52, 53, 95, 97

Valle, José, 41
Venezuela, 38, 52, 93, 95, 97, 101
venom, 41, 67-72
Vick, James, 68-72

waggle dance, 150
Wall Street Journal, 22
Wasbauer, Marius, 104
Washington Post, 93
wasps, 130-31
Wilson, William, 136, 137-40
Wisconsin, 54
worker bees, 65, 146, 151
"World of Survival," 109
Wulfrath, Juan, 102
Wyoming, 136

Yucatán, 102, 118

Zimmer, Robert W., 129